REMINDING
ME OF MO

A MEMOIR

GABRIEL
PATTERSON

PUBLISHING

REMINDING ME OF MO

Copyright © 2021 by Gabriel Patterson

Contact Info: gabrieljpatterson@hotmail.com

Book Cover Design by: Pries for Pries Designs

Author Photo by: Stephanie Patterson for Amethyst Star Photography

Cover Photo Courtesy of: St. Charles Recreation Center, Denver, CO

Editor: Marlowe at Authors AI

Formatting Template: Brady Moller

ISBN: 978-1-7366072-0-6 (paperback) 978-1-7366072-1-3 (ebook)

978-1-7366072-2-0 (audiobook)

Library of Congress Cataloging-in-Publication Data

Patterson, Gabriel

Reminding Me of Mo / by Gabriel Patterson 1-10178196611

First Edition: March 2021

10 9 8 7 6 5 4 3 2 1

CONTENTS

AUTHOR'S NOTE

This book was made to honor the life of my friend, Geranimo Maestas. It is not intended to propagate violence, nor revise the past. It is not meant to guilt any individual or entity. It is a living document, testament, and sacrament. It is both my recollection of the past and interpretation of the facts, and is not meant to be unequivocal or devout, although by its very nature, it is most certainly unequivocal and devout. Throughout the book, Hip Hop is spelled with capital letters because it is the name of our culture. "Hip" means to know. "Hop" means to move. Thus, we know *why* we move. Such is the case of the *No 'Mo Violence Movement.* Names have been changed to protect identities.

AUTHOR'S NOTE

THE 826 EXPERIMENT

826 WAS A RAUCOUS RIDE in years past and this year will be no different. Our new bus driver, Shirley, isn't intimidated by a bunch of Mexicans but quickly earns our respect. We appreciate that she keeps a silver boombox in tow, meticulously wedged between dash and window. The airwaves of KS104 keep our attention and Shirley makes no secret of her crush on Bobby Brown, who controls the airwaves of contemporary radio in 1989. Shirley pulls to the curb and cranks the door handle.

Mo and Pablo wait at the front of the line to claim the coveted seats at the back of the bus. Everyone else is scattered about, so I inch closer. Mo has a cool about him, wearing black stonewashed jeans with a pristine pair of Jordans. Pablo is wearing a long-sleeved shirt with shorts, an odd combination, but nobody says anything to him about it. Mo twirls a Chicago Bulls pencil in hand and notices me focused on the logo.

"You don't like the Nuggets?"

"Of course I do, but Jordan is the best player in the league." Mo responds.

"Not Larry Bird?"

"Larry Bird!" Mo chimes. But his awareness stops himself before expounding any further. He laughs in a high register then turns to Pablo who shakes his head and smiles, dismissing me without even having to speak on it.

"I like the Nuggets but they can't beat Showtime. Even at fifty-two eighty, we're still playing four games at the Forum and Showtime always shows up at the Forum." He holds out his fist and says, "I'm Geranimo."

"What's up, I'm Gabriel," trying to sound cool as we bump fists.

"This is Pablo." Mo says, introducing me to the behemoth on his side. Pablo then gives me a dap that reverberates my body and that is that. Mo never says I can hang with them but mentions their plan to mash to the back of the bus and I tell myself that no matter what, I will follow.

As Shirley turns onto 38th I expound to Mo and Pablo about the injustice done to me by my dad. "His job gave him tickets to the Nuggets and Lakers at McNichols but instead of taking me he took my uncle. Nope, never forgave him. Still don't. My one time to see Earvin 'Magic' Johnson—he hit the game winner no doubt!"

"Well it's not like you missed Jordan or somethin'."

"Will you quit with Jordan already? He can't even get past the Pistons."

"That's alright, he's on *George Michael's Sports Machine* every night. Hey, you wanna play 21 after school with me and Pablo?"

"Yeah, what rules do you do?"

"Make it/take it. Two-hand tips for minus two, one-hand zero. One-point shots from the top until a miss. No takin' it back after a miss."

"You don't take it back after a miss?"

"Nah," Mo said, lettin' me know it wasn't up for discussion. His court, his rules.

But we move when the bus moves. Shirley's wide mirror is perfectly positioned to catch us in the act, for moving while the bus is in motion is the most egregious violation in her view. Yet Mo waits until Shirley executes a long buttonhook turn then glides seamlessly into a girl's seat, convincing her of her own adolescent beauty, risking a referral just to dote on her for a while. Of course, we all have bus reputations to uphold. Pablo, who has the upper body of an Olympic weightlifter, is the muscle. All he has to do is merely sit by a kid who's talkin' stuff, sixty seconds later the kid is whimpering from Pablo's physical prowess.

Inside this steel tube we feel invincible. 826 is our Japanese slow-bullet train. Its windows reflecting pictographs, namely a mural of Aztlan, when we hook a left from 42nd Avenue onto Tejon Street. Another right onto 38th Ave, passing the brown brick fire station then a left on Federal. We pass Botanica Yemaya, Woodbury Library, and North High School. On further down Federal Blvd during the entire morning show and all the music, including the "Were you in a recent accident commercials." Now passing Barnum Park and Columbine Steak House. Further down as adolescent boys rubberneck the entrance to Dandy Dan's while exceedingly more mature girls roll their eyes. We pass Chinatown and nope, still not there yet. We begin trading Hoops cards to pass the time. Conversations include the ins and outs of the greatest game ever invented. Green seats become tapestries we populate with jumbo letter font. Nicknames are etched in pencil lead. Bold letters appear from permanent markers written by dudes who crave initiation into a gang.

North Denver to Littleton is like taking us to Oz. The treacherous journey is longer than the 30 and 31 routes of RTD combined. We still do the knowledge. And recess. And the rest of it. We jump off the bus jetlagged, but the bumper-to-bumper traffic won't grind us to a halt. We ask our parents if we can go to school in our own neighborhood, but they tell us to just deal with it. Nobody tells us it's enforced by the state, a result of Keyes v. Denver School District 1, and that some in Denver were so opposed to busing, they exploded buses at the bus depot. That was twenty years ago, and it still impacts all of Denver's neighborhoods. Our side of town is brown, so this forced merging of neighborhoods means anything can happen. Yet riding across town our pride is strong, hopefully we aren't greeted with a bomb.

The best part of 826 is this newfound friendship. Mo and Pablo two titans of 826, and me, hoping to infuse some sophistication to their coolness. We spill onto school grounds with Pro-Keds and British Knights. Mo is last off the bus, dismissing the final two stairs and jump-stopping his introduction into a new world. Walking toward the entrance I ask Mo and Pablo about their homeroom.

"You guys in Ms. Baumbach's class?"

"Damn, me and Pablo both got Vigil, we'll catch up at lunch though. You on free-lunch?"

I had forgotten the Free-Lunch Program certified credibility but pivoted quick, "Oh, well, you know bro, I brought my lunch today," diverting the fact that I must buy my lunch. My coolness waning fast but instead of ousting me, Mo roasted me:

"Hey, *this* crazy fool brought his own lunch to school!" Which resulted in another disapproval from Pablo, who shook his head and through his clenched teeth, let out a "Sssss."

The lawn edges at Kaiser are tight. Perfectly rounded trees with Crayola green grass suspended in white concrete trapezoids. Behind the school is no uneven gravel and broken glass shards like at the bus stop. Their field has a gazebo at the hilltop, highlighting rows of posh mini mansions with erect mailboxes. We enter this stargate known as 826 and emerge on the other side. Most feel we're not supposed to see it, that it's too foreign, and that *we* are too foreign. Nevertheless, the ace up the sleeve

4

belongs to us, for the keeper of this futuristic landscape—Humberto—rides with us on 826 to maintain its allure.

We step in feeling free. Aqua Netted up. Eons away from our parents. (Do they know where they're taking us?) At lunchtime, neither group has the courage to befriend each other nor extend a hand, for even if we do intermingle, half of us will go home on 826 so it doesn't matter.

Three o'clock approaches and I wonder if the guys will remember me. Will they do a 180? Will Pablo finally decide to speak to me? Hell, they don't even know if I can play yet, but to my surprise, when I climb the three steps onto the bus they're already at the back. Mo waves for me to come on and Pablo—like some type of bouncer—stands in the aisle guarding the two by one seats and moves aside as I roll through. Now we're a trio.

"How was it?" Mo asks.

"What? School? Yeah, it was cool."

"Good, cause ya' mind has to be right for this game were 'bout to run."

That comment has Pablo smiling and the game is afoot.

Shirley lets us get loud. The radio plays jams and it's not long before homework flies out the window. After another momentous trek she drops us off and I follow the guys to just before Pecos Street, where we cut down an alley. Mo grabs his basketball. Next, we throw our school folders on the concrete and it's on. Squeaks only happen in gyms. Out here it's stomps, footsteps and jumpstops. The game is fastpaced and rough. I can't break through Pablo's smothering defense and when I do, Mo scrapes my shot with not much effort, deflecting it as it falls short of the rim.

Mo's eyes are intense, he's both athletic and intelligent on the court. Pablo resembles the Tasmanian Devil. No doubt they are warriors who don't give an inch and stakes are high, reputations are on the line that could last a lifetime. After the first game I'm bent over heaving, hands over my knees, wondering if they'll reject me, finishing with a point total of negative 8. Was my basketball IQ high enough for Mo? Was I physical enough for Pablo? I look up and see Mo walking toward me, sweat beads trickling down both sides of his face. He taps me twice on the back and with a steady breath says, "C'mon, brother, let's run it back."

ALLINIT

JACKIN' IS AT AN ALL-TIME high. If that fool Tom Brokaw wants to make a change in something that has to do with us, start there. Leave our emcees alone. We don't call anyone "bully." There's just jackers and full-time jack moves. Recreation centers are safe though, and for Mo, this specifically means St. Charles Recreation Center. He always talks about it, describing the ballers at St. Charles and how they come from around the city to sharpen skills. But Mo's done reminiscing this morning. He suggests we go down there. I'm fighting the idea.

"But bro, why we gotta ride across the whole city to play ball? We can do that right here, or we can hit Smedley . . . or Aztlan."

"C'mon, man, nobody's gonna mess with us. It'll be fun. This is loong overdue."

"Where we gonna park our bikes?"

"Who cares?!"

"But we don't have no locks."

"St. Charles is cool, man. We don't need no locks. Truss me. I wanna introduce you to everybody."

I appreciate Mo's confidence but sometimes broad daylight ain't even a safe bet, especially if you want to keep your bike.

They might jack you just for the sake of jackin' you. But Mo's belief that nothing was gonna happen meant nothing was gonna happen. So when I swiped my dad's cycling cap, Mo let me rock it without judgement. So off we went, two homies on two bikes. It would've definitely helped us by having Pablo come but he had to help his dad with something.

Denver's streets are affiliated. We're not even hip to what this means, so we imagine wearing 3-D glasses with blue and red lenses where gangstas pop out of dimensions like ghosts, and Slimer throws gangs signs. Not everybody follows the classic examples of blue and red. Other gangs make their own colors with the teams on top. Denver Bronco gear should be neutral but it's not. Gangs fuck that up too. So how we supposed to be fans without gear? I guess Mo had the plan with the pencils. Nobody's gonna jack us for a pencil or a pencil sharpener, but you never know.

Red and blue are the colors of the Pepsi plant we pass on our way to St. Charles. We ride uphill, downhill, over broken glass shards and through steel structures. We arrive at St. Charles and it's just how Mo describes it: warm and friendly. An elder outside the front door is excited to see him.

"Hey Mo! Haven't seen you in a while, son, everything good?"

"Yeah, we moved to the North Side but I'm still hoopin' every day, Rich."

"That's good to hear. Cause all your crew be up here every day too, and they're also getting better."

"That's good," Mo says, nodding his head and smiling, "maybe they'll catch me one day."

"Boy I see your confidence hasn't waned none. Who's this?"

"This is my homie Gabe. I brought him to show him the gym."

"Oh, nice to meet 'ya G. Well come on in, I don't wanna hold you guys up."

We enter and Mo politics with more elders at the front desk.

Everyone is upbeat and has positive vibes. I can see why this is the spot for Mo.

We roll up on a dude at the corner table working solo shot on a jigsaw puzzle. From behind he looks like a child. He's focused on the task at hand but when Mo slaps him on the shoulder it breaks his concentration. When he sees Mo, he smiles. His eyes are crossed naturally, and his head is shaped like a box, but it springs in excitement from the recognition Mo lays on him. This kid looks like an outcast, but Mo saw people, and that meant he saw Telley.

"Geranimo, where you been, hermano? The center's not the same without you. And school, too."

"We moved away but I'm back today. What you up to, Telley?"

"I've been working on this all day. Looks good, no? I have these edges set. You guys wanna help?"

"Not right now, Telley. We came to hoop."

"Oh, okay then. Score a lotta hoops, guys."

I'm surprised we didn't hit the gym first but now I know this is a reunion. Mo left a bunch when he moved to the North Side. A whole community of elders and kids, team players and volunteers.

The pounding basketball and squeakin' sneakers sound louder and louder as we make our way to the gym.

A kid bumps Mo's shoulder intentionally and spouts off, "HEY HOMIE! WATCH WHERE YOU WALKIN'!"

Mo turns around but is intercepted by Rich.

"Hey, hey, hey, chill out, Derrick. We don't do that type of stuff in here, son. And the black bandana's gotta go, either put it away or you can't be in here."

"Hey! THAT fool bumped into ME."

"Now don't play me like that, Derrick. Your brother Dion used to come in here all the time. I can call him if you want."

"You'll have to call the County, gee."

"Awe Derrick, I didn't know. He was a great athlete, I'm sorry."

"I'm not, he ain't no big brother to me. Fuck that foo—"

"ALRIGHT THAT'S IT! You can't talk like that in here! One more warning and you're out!"

"Whateva gee, calm down. *You* the one asking about Dion. I'm not his dad . . ."

Not wanting to deal with Derrick any further Rich walks off. This kid is about the drama and they're giving him a lot of rope. But they must figure if this dude can't be at St. Charles, where else is he gonna go?

I turn around before we enter the gym and Derrick is still staring at us. Staring hard too. But once in the gym Mo smiles like we're standing on sacred ground.

I love that he's immune to this crazy fool, but this guy has me shitted. I've never been in a squabble and I don't want to be in one today. Mo walks smoothly as if navigating a minefield and starts jabbing at the six dudes playin' half-court 21. Of course he knows each one and their skill set. Mo asks me if I want to partake.

"Nah, I think I'm just gonna watch."

"Come on, man, we didn't come here for you to not get down."

"Alright then."

I act like I'm playin' defense but really I'm watchin' the entrance of the gym as if this fool will come barreling around the corner.

Maybe he's mad he couldn't bait Mo into a squabble. Or maybe some kids are just born to start shit.

Whatever the case, Mo operates on another plane. He's not afraid to remain confident.

Later, Mo's at game point and I'm thankful this fool hasn't shown his face in the gym yet.

We finish the game, say goodbyes but hear yelling in the hallway. It's Derrick, of course.

Somebody took the bait. I don't even want to look but move with the group into the hall. Mo has no part of the elders kicking Derrick out, and stands at the gym entrance with old friends, watching the commotion of elders who are threatening Derrick and another kid—who must've entered the center after we hit the gym—with calling the cops. Thankfully, that's the only thing getting them to leave. Derrick's partner in crime has a black bandana hanging from his back pocket but Rich and the elders are less concerned with the bandana and more set on throwing those two out.

Mo's friend says something funny and Mo starts laughing, it's not even about those two wannabes, but Derrick feels that Mo is laughing at him and doesn't take it lightly. He yells at Mo again.

"WHAT THA FUCK U LAUGHIN' AT, FOOL!"

But Derrick's partner in crime gets him to flee.

"C'MON D-MONEY, WE NEED TO JET BEFORE THE COPS COME!"

They slide out. The front doors of the center slam shut, and we can see the frustration in the elders.

"This is a safe place, man. What's happening?" says Rich to another elder.

"I agree, but it's getting harder to keep the riff raff out and keep the good ones in . . ."

Mo tells me later that Derrick was never good at sports. Derrick's brother Dion however, played against Mo and even showed him a couple moves, being that he was older. Dion teased Derrick in grade school that he threw like a girl, but once D-Money joined something called Tha Throwz, or 2T for short, he became untouchable.

I ask Mo if we can call someone for a ride back to his house, it's worth a shot.

"I don't want to head out there, those fools might be hiding in the bushes or some shit."

"What do you mean, man? We can do anything we want; go anywhere we want to go. Don't worry about all that." Well, if Mo says we're good then we're good. Rich walks us outside when Mo tells him we're about to be Audi 5000. Rich stands with his hands on his hips as we mount our bikes.

"Don't worry about him coming back, guys. He'd be foolish to come back here. And if he does, he betta act right... Alright Mo, great to see ya, man. Come back anytime."

"Will do."

"Nice to meet ya, G."

"You, too."

And Rich walks inside.

Mo wasn't gonna waste time and worry about a wannabe with evil in his eyes. He had a city to explore and cassette tapes to play.

"So what did you think of St. Charles?" Mo asks, unaffected by the drama.

"Yo, I really dug it!" And I did. Seeing the excitement in Mo's eyes made me forget about the ruckus. I'm happy he took me there, and I did feel safe. Nothing bad ever happens when I'm with Mo.

"I knew you would. Now, race you to the crib! . . ."

And Mo zooms off on his bike. I follow as quickly as I can and stay on his back wheel for most of the way.

When we're close to Mo's at around 40th & Osage we see a bunch of dudes on the corner in orange, green and white. People rockin' Miami Hurricanes shit in Denver? What's that about? Wait—they're mean-muggin' and stompin' toward us. *Fast.* We turn around and jet, realizing that what we dodged in the East is the same beast with different colors in the North. We pedal hard while rubbernecking these dudes from our bikes. The group laughs and points. One launches a 40 at us that glides through the sky in a perfect spiral. It shatters behind us, but we keep pedaling. Eventually, the Miami Hurricane dudes are out of view.

I'M YOUR PUSHER

MO IS THE TASTEMAKER, the DJ, Hip Hop connoisseur, and his rotation is hard to crack: Kid N' Play's *2 Hype*, Heavy D & The Boyz' *Big Tyme*, Eazy-E's *Eazy Duz It*, and of course the *Power* album by Ice-T. The first time we ever heard of a natural high is from an Ice-T record. Ain't that somethin'? In this infamous new era of "Parental Advisory" stickers, the phrase only means that Mo advises his parents to buy him the newest, rawest, most groundbreaking music of the day. But do-gooders are busy trying to grasp the idea of gangsta rap and whether or not it's a passing fad. Of the three major networks, one in particular focuses on gangsta rap morning, noon, and night. NBC's Tom Brokaw delivers reports cautioning parents of violence and misogyny in the lyrics but luckily, our parents don't flinch. There's an emcee named Ice on the scene, and not the one you may be thinking of. This one has more hustler in his speech, we bump it nonstop.

The lyrics are printed out so we can follow along. Ice ain't hiding from nobody. So like broken glass to bare feet, or a razor-blade to a jump rope, these words become swords young fans like us wield to the controlling systems, whether they be on the news or in the classroom.

"Ice-T is Superman," says Mo, "and his posse, Rhyme Syndicate, is the Justice League. Tell that fool Tom Brokaw he should skate!" Ice-T's *Power* album is replete with powerful messages about freedom of speech and even includes harsh warnings of the life. Out of the bunch, Mo plays it the most. More sophisticated than the rest, an overview of the game if you will, steering us in the right direction without being preachy.

Side B begins with Ice-T in the middle of a transaction. But where the buyer asks for something illegal, Ice promises dopeness in the form of a 12" record. Mo loves the message he makes, even though politicians want to take down the messenger. Either way, the emcee proceeds to call crack stupid, adding that when he's on the mic spittin' dope rhymes, no beepers are needed.

"I bet'cha Ice-T does more good with his music than the 'Say No to Drugs' campaign can," Mo quips, but his taste in music is as eclectic as the groups in the rap world. His favorite line by far is from Hev's "We Got Our Own Thang," but Mo switches it up:

"Throwing down lyrics like you throw down a flapjack,
you're a chicken-fried nugget and I'm a Big Stack!"

That line is his go-to on the basketball court, tetherball, and four square. He drains a shot over your outstretched hand: *"you're a chicken-fried nugget and I'm a Big Stack!"* He ousts you in Four Square by inching the ball across a heavily guarded corner: *"you're a chicken-fried nugget and I'm a Big Stack!"* All that is left for you is to stand pat and watch that maroon ball roll into oblivion. But Mo also reserves a completely neurotic yell which induces psychological warfare on the court. The exuberant, "Owwwwwwwwww," with corresponding head gyrations Mo reserves for those days when he's in a zone and we can't stop him. Mo will look Pablo dead in the face and head-juke left, crossover right, drive to the rim right hand cupping the rock, pivoting on a dime and watch Pablo bite on the pump fake, calling bank before the shot. Next came, "Owwwwwwwwww!" Sometimes Pablo—physical prowess notwithstanding—just smiles and knows he has to take whatever Mo is dishing if he can't stop him. Pablo musters a laugh sometimes, though clearly frustrated at Mo's relentless taunts. But that's how it is on the court: To the winner go the spoils.

* * *

Saturday morning begins like all the other Saturday mornings— watching Hip Hop videos. The living room in Mo's house flaunts two circular bucket seats with a table in between. We're enveloped in the big-pinned cushions of the bucket seats when Mo journeys to the kitchen to look for cereal. He then walks back into the living room.

"What we havin'?" I ask Mo, my eyes glued to the TV, but he walks by, ignoring my question then pounds on Cathy's room a couple times.

"Mom, we don't have no cereal!"

"Take some money from my purse and go to the corner store, baby."

We know Cathy likes to sleep in on weekends and are more than down to venture into the crisp overcast morning. Parlaying to the store for cereal is an important task for two homies. I inhale deeply, holding my breath as Mo's hand enters Cathy's purse, and as if performing surgery, I don't exhale until his hand completely removes her wallet. The screen door clangs against the door jam and we were out, Mo clutching the folded dollars in his hand like a hawk snatch. A makeshift store sits on the corner 40th & Pecos, one block south of the halfway house.

The halfway house is two levels high. Its yard area is surrounded by a low fence, so anyone walking by can see those dudes posted up smoking cigarettes. They look more confused than mean, but then their confusion is scarier than anything we've seen.

"What's up, little homies. Where ya headed?" says a dude in the yard but we don't answer. Instead, we look at each other, wondering why this fool gives a damn about us or where we're going. We're not ignoring the dude; we just don't know what type of answer will suffice.

"WELL FORGET YOU GUYS, THEN!" Says the dude and I start walking faster, not wanting to turn around or make eye contact. Mo turns around and starts walking backwards to keep eyes on the homie, who knows if he'll jump the fence or what. We continue at an accelerated pace. I ask Mo if we're cool.

"Yeah, he's just looking at us, probably mad that he can't leave," Mo reassures, "we're ok."

We finally reach our destination. It's a rundown market made of dirty red bricks. The food aisle is bleak, but they have what we need, Mo's go-to: Cap 'N Crunch. When the clerk gives Mo the total, he tallies the dollars in his fist and inches out a few extras, grabbing a handful of Atomic Fireballs and placing 'em on the counter next to the cereal. On the way back we muse about what time we think Pablo might show up and hope that videos will still be rolling during breakfast.

"Nah bro, I don't wanna walk by that halfway house again."

"Ah man, forget that dude. We'll tell him we're on a nature walk or somethin'."

When we return to the house Mo places two bowls on the table between the big-pinned cushions then clinks a spoon into each. He pours Cap N' Crunch to the brim of his bowl and hands the box to me. Slowly poured milk elevates his cereal above the rim creating a mound of orange morsel goodness. Mo begins eating a spoonful while balancing the bowl in his left hand. I hurry and pour my cereal too. Mo's brother Ray Ray stumbles out of his room wiping his eye and stands smack dab in front of the TV. Instead of Mo yelling at Ray Ray to get out the way, he asks him if he wants some cereal.

"Yes, please."

"Well go get a bowl and spoon then."

Ray Ray dutifully returns while the black and white polka-dotted wears of Heavy D's "We Got Our Own Thang" comes on the screen. I glance down and—Shit! —there's a roach in my cereal! It's a smaller one albeit, but a roach, nonetheless. My thoughts race. Why did we buy cereal from an unkempt store? Why couldn't there have been a Safeway nearby? Hell, if I would've known what would've come flying out of that cereal box, I would have talked Mo into hoofing it the ten blocks to Safeway on 48th. The cereal was probably there for ages!

Mo catches me looking down at my cereal and with a mouthful of Cap-N-Crunch mumbles something to the effect of, "S'good, right?!"

"Yeah," I reply hesitantly, not wanting to ruin his breakfast but also not warning him like, "Dude, check your cereal for roaches!" Instead I freeze. My appetite gone. Now how to sneak this cereal into the kitchen to dump without getting a lecture from Mo about wasting the Cap 'N Crunch?

After heaving my cereal into the trash can and strategically placing some trash over the mess, I come back from the kitchen and slide into my bucket seat with the big-pinned cushion without making a sound. The guilt of not saying anything begins to swell inside of me and I tell Mo about the roach. He takes his eyes off the TV to look at me, still gnashing his teeth on Cap 'N Crunch as milk coats the edges of his lips. Grinning slightly, he says, "Did you pluck it out?"

ROSARY BEADS

MO DESIRES COMPETITION. He wants to eat, sleep, and breathe basketball. He'll greet anyone upon entry to the court, from the privileged kids on the South Side to the skilled ballers on the East. If he's walking down a block dribbling a pale orange dot, he thinks he should be immune to neighborhood politics. This attitude might get us in a beef but I'm rolling with Mo regardless. He's the glue, connecting people who would otherwise be disconnected, like Pablo and I. We look up to Mo, but Mo looks up to his dad, Ray Sr. It's not that Ray Ray is his favorite, despite bestowing Mo's little brother with his name, it's just that sometimes he sees Mo, and sometimes not.

Mo's dad is a mystifying character who embodies both the warrior look of Native American legends and is also a picturesque depiction of the alpha male in our beloved brown pride murals. Yet at only 5'6", Ray Sr. relies on his gristle voice and charisma to navigate this world and lead his family. He has the chiseled chest, a handlebar mustache, slicked hair, and dons black zoot suit pants with a pressed, heavy cotton all black t-shirt. His gold medallion is a simplistic but heavy cross that sways as he walks. Though Mo, Pablo and I are almost as tall as him, Ray Sr. is a larger than life figure who only appears at night, for the evening is his domain. To see Ray during the day is a rare occurrence, like spotting a celebrity at the grocery store. Nevertheless, we see Ray Sr. rolling with a friend in a rectangular box of a Buick in the alley. We pause our game and say what's up.

"What's up is me and Ernesto gotta hit the East Side, you boys down to roll?"

"You know it!" Mo chimes enthusiastically.

We jump onto the burgundy velvet of those cushiony seats and the only thing that belongs in our age is a cassette deck in place of what can easily have been an 8-track player. As we pick up speed heading east on 38th Avenue, packaged steel cutting through the Denver breeze, what comes on but "Tell Her," by El Chicano. What?! I couldn't let this opportunity fly by. This was the one time I could one-up Mo and Pablo and certify my music cred. The only reason I knew the song is my dad would play it.

"This is El Chicano." I say confidently to Ray Sr, Ernesto, Mo, and Pablo.

"Who?" Mo says, ears raised and intent on knowing what the elders in the car already know, landing in uncharted territory where he—the soul controller and owner of cool—is the one late to the party.

"Don't you know who El Chicano is?!" I bark. I can't match Pablo on knowledge of Vicente Fernandez, and I can't match Mo on Hip Hop, but I got them both on this one.

Surprisingly, Ray Sr. is on my side. "He's right Mo, this is that good music from back in the day where they still played instruments."

"Yeah, well I'd rather listen to some dope rhymes over a fly beat!" Not hearing any of what Ray Sr. was sayin'.

We don't get out of the car on the East Side. Ray Sr. leaves the car idling and we're chillin' with Ernesto who's not much of a talker. As Ray Sr. walks to the front door of an old brick house we watch his moves, breathing, and the ease with which he steps.

He then disappears into the house. We look to our left and sprawled out on a porch is four dudes. Three of them have black bandanas hanging from their back pockets while one has it wrapped around the bottom of his face, showing only his eyes. They're looking right at us.

I sink into the seat and ask Mo, "Remember Derek?"

"Who?"

"You know, Derek, D-Money? That dude tryin' to sweat you at the center."

"That dude didn't sweat me."

"I'm just sayin' he had a black bandana too!"

"These guys ain't about nothing. Besides, we have Ernesto. Right?"

"That's right, Mo," answers Ernesto, and as he turns to look at us, Mo hands him the *Power* tape.

"A bandana don't make you hard," Ernesto adds.

Somehow, the machismo I'm surrounded by is soothing. I can expect it from these gangstas, and I can expect it from Ernesto—he's the elder in this situation—but then Pablo chimes in.

"Man, those wannabe gangstas are thinner than your muscles," as Pablo pinches my bicep with his middle finger and thumb.

Ernesto turns around adding, "Don't worry little man," and proceeds to pop the glovebox. "I got somethin' for ya." He hands a pair of brass knuckles over the elongated barrier of the Buick's front seat. I take them in my hand and can't think of anything to say but, "damn, these are heavy!"

"You would say that" Pablo says as he snatches them from my hand.

Pablo puts them on his fist then Mo says, "Let me see."

Right then Ray Sr. opens the door and says, "Put those things away, Mo."

"We good, Ray?" asks Ernesto.

"Yeah, let's go," Ray responds. He looks to his left then adds, "What's going on over here?"

"Just a bunch of punk kids, hermano, that's all."

To prove a point, Ray Sr. drives by real slow and maddoggs 'em while doing so. They don't say shit to Ray Sr. He looks the part—one badass dude they don't want to fuck with. And thank God, who knows what could've happened if we weren't with adults. Yet as soon as they're in the rear view, and the three of us look out the back window, one of them slumps to the middle of the street. Throwing signs, of course. It didn't matter we had two adults in the car, they were ready. Maybe even locked and loaded. But by the time we get to Mo's their posturing is a faded memory, and now we're bumpin' the *Power* tip.

We have plans for the night. All of Mo's family are going to the movies and me and Pablo are invited. The sun falls as we head back to Pecos Street. Ray Sr. drops us at home for dinner and will come get us when it's time for the movie. We hop out and Mo asks his dad for his tape. Ray Sr. begins bartering.

"Hey son, let me and Ernesto jam it for a while. We'll be right back, we just gotta make another stop real quick. You'll have it back when we go to the movies, son."

"You mean you don't wanna bump El Chicano anymore?" Mo jabs, letting out a chuckle. He got us, but Ray Sr. says it best.

"Well, son, I may be older, but I'm still fly. We like that hard-core too."

"I got stuff harder than—"

"No, Mo, this will do."

"Alright, then," and the three of us shake hands with the adults for once, holding up our chins while we do it too.

* * *

We scatter over the drive-in gravel like a bursting piñata: Festive, exuberant. Perched on the merry-go-round waiting intently for

Bobby Brown's cameo. The Cinderella City Drive-In is our crosstown venture for *Ghostbusters II*. We're thick. And when I say thick, I mean we're deep. Mo, Pablo, Ray Ray, La La, Ray Sr, Cathy, Estevan, Ernesto, and Gustavo. We mob to concessions like the fury of a tornado. A tub of popcorn for all the kids to share. We each grab a jump rope licorice and split, movie already playing, the scene where Oscar is swept away in his carriage by the electromagnetic slime. The drive-in theater's radios crackle as gravel crunches under our feet. As the movie plays my eyes escape the screen to look at the stars. They're magical, the universe is like a canopy over us. Our ankles dangle off the edge of the merry-go-round, feet suspended in air while Mo sits next to me on the other side of the arm bar. Pablo sits in a lawn chair while Mo jokes about the movie, forever our narrator in moviegoing or life. Brown bodies hang off the merry-go-round like another constellation in the Milky Way. Everything is peace and love when we get home, but it won't be long before there is chaos.

* * *

Someone pissed off Ray Sr. and they shut down the club. They stepped on his shoes and he lost it. They kept walkin' and didn't turn around, didn't even apologize: *the ultimate disrespect.* Activating that rage inside him. It's a David Banner scenario. When Ray Sr. catches the dude that stepped on his shoes in the parking lot, he snatches the guy's heart out of his chest and bails. One-hundred cops are dispersed throughout Denver to hunt him down. They bring out the guns that shoot weighted nets, that is, assuming their police cruisers can keep pace. The Emergency Broadcast System wails and this is not a drill. It is not noon on a Wednesday and Denver Public School lunch lines are not serving slopped spaghetti. Ray Sr. grabs the veins of the city and won't let go. Someone stepped on his shoes at Muñeca's and it's on!

Danger is abound. Karl Mecklenberg locks himself inside his own house. Gabo sends a distress call to Cathy and she pushes the off button to the Curtis Mathis, rounds up us kids and makes a beeline to the kitchen. We wait for about thirty seconds as she rummages through the house, returning to the kitchen with candles. She slides out a kitchen drawer and reaches into the back of it. Three quarters of her arm is lost underneath the counter when she pulls out a string of rosary beads. Noticing fear in my face she hands them to me, "Here mijo, these will keep you safe." Gabo calls again. He was following Ray Sr.'s rage but lost it at the Car Wash overlooking the dip in 38th Avenue that connects LoDo to the North Side. "Be careful," he says, "keep the kids safe, Cathy, I'm on my way." We stand in a candlelit circle and I clutch the dark maroon rosary beads like my life depends on it. Never had communion, never went to church, and can't recite the Lord's Prayer. "We'll have to drop the 'frigerator on him to slow him down," Mo quips. And with no other input his idea makes sense. This is our bomb shelter plan. The threat of Cold War USSR is nothing compared to Ray Sr. flipping the fuck out. This is what we're afraid of, that person who has the knowl-edge, the vernacular and the prowess but is overwhelmed when they realize their own power—that's Ray Sr. to a tee. Mo has the Jesus candle with the flaming heart. La La has the Virgin Mary and Ray Ray is swathed up in Cathy's robe clutching her leg while Pablo holds a butcher's knife. All the lights are off but for our glowing séance. This is our hope, that at one look our inno-cence will snap Ray Sr. out of his rage. I might as well pray so I clutch the rosary beads with two hands and hold them against my chest and just as I'm about to close my eyes, Cathy says, "Look at Gabe, my mijo is breathing so hard it looks like he's having a heart attack!" Everyone sees me panting hard and burst into laughter. They laugh so hard that I start laughing, too. Humor again relieves the tension in our bodies.

After about an hour or so, we're sitting on the kitchen floor.

Mo asks if we can go to his room and Cathy obliges. Pablo comes at me again as soon as we're in Mo's room.

"Why you always scared every time somethin' happens, man?" says Pablo.

"You weren't scared?"

"Nah."

I turn to Mo. "You think your dad's gonna make it home?"

"Wherever he is, he'll be alright," Mo says confidently, then quickly changes the subject. "I'm thirsty."

We all head up for some water before bed. By now it's a safe bet that Ray Sr. won't make it home. The eyes of Jesus and Mary watch us intensely, candles still aflame upon the kitchen table.

EL GRITO

21. AND WE PREFER THE STREET rule of tips: Any missed shot by an opponent can be hurled back into the hoop if your feet aren't touching the ground. This results in a two-point loss for your opponent if you use two hands. Or you can reset your opponent's score at zero if you tap in their miss with one hand. If you already have zero, your score can go negative by two points or by ten, depending on how many hands were used on the tip in. These added rules infuse excitement into our games. I usually hog the three-point line on offense because I'm sick of Mo and Pablo blocking my shot, or as we call it, "sending that shit back!" The beginnings of our games flow quickly until Mo or Pablo reach game point, which is usually 19, (we tally 2-points per bucket, with the top of the key shots equaling 1-point after a 2-point make in the field.) Even 18 is occasionally game point for Mo and Pablo, because they can easily drain that long shot from the top of the key and end the game. A normal scenario puts Mo at a point total of 19, Pablo at around 17 and me, hovering around a meager 9 points. I win one out of every thirty games, which is not bad by the scope of things. Maybe the guys are only tired one out of every thirty games.

I'm sick of losing, anybody would be if they lost this much. Finally, I concoct a plan so farfetched, so obtuse, that not even I can understand how it will work or how gullible Mo will have to be for me to execute it. It involves the one thing I can champion, the one thing I can brag about, a domain where I alone am king: *running*. It's endurance for endurance's sake. A scroll of seamless poetry. Staking the coals and keeping the train moving. No jab-steps or jump-stops or hot-dogging or trash talk or game-points or Jordans. Just the race against time and timelessness. The reason Nike was created. (Despite being overshadowed by that pale orange dot.) (Okay, you get the point.) I was going to make Mo pay for his basketball dominance, for his on-court acumen, and for all his trash talk that I stowed away in my subconscious. There was a reason I arrived to the court with Asics and Cross Trainers as opposed to that Jumpman logo on Mo's tongue, and now he had to learn why.

My dad introduced me to these 5k jaunts as a weekend task and we kept at them. Most of the 5k runs took place in South Denver or way out in Littleton, but a particular race was set in our own backyard of North Denver. The location: Sloan's Lake. The event: El Grito. All I had to do now was work on Mo to come around to the idea of running the race with me. First, I must isolate him. I know from the jump that I ain't going to invite Pablo because Pablo will give us a serious run for our money. Besides, if Pablo beats us both, where will that leave me? I can't take that chance. My opening is the in between times, when Pablo has to abide by his father's curfew and head home for the night.

Pablo's home life isn't like mine or Mo's. His father is strict. He disapproves of sleep overs and frankly, us. Mo and I saw the inside of Pablo's house only once and that was a couple days ago when our bus broke down in route to pick us up.

"What we gonna do now?"

"We can chill at my house for a while."

"What? You're serious, bro?!"

"Yeah, my dad's at work."

It was the only time we saw Pablo squirm. We wouldn't let him rest. Mo and I kept picking up knickknacks and putting them back.

"It's like your dad keeps track of where things are." I said teasingly.

"He does."

Then Pablo put his hand on my shoulder blade and began to squeeze as I exposed the folded edge of a towel uncovering a stack of tortillas.

"Ow!" I called as I replaced the flap. Out we went from Pablo's house, as quickly as we went in.

Pablo was later grounded for letting us in the house. He told us he confessed, probably reasoning a preemptive admission would result in less contempt from his father than an admission after the fact. But this was all the time I needed, perfect timing to execute my plan.

I didn't tell Mo that my Dad already signed him up for El Grito or that both of our race shirts sat atop my dresser. It took some begging, but most of all, I had to validate the "coolness" of the race experience for Mo.

"Seven? I don't wake up until eight on the weekends."

"But c'mon, man, it'll be fun, my folks will give us a ride. They have free ice cream after the race too."

"Yeah, but I'd rather be eating Cap N' Crunch watching TV."

"But bro, Pablo's grounded so we're not gonna play basketball. Let's do it, I promise it'll be fun."

"Okay but call me first."

The next morning, I dial Mo but get Cathy instead.

Boyyy!! . . . what'cha calling for so early?!!

But Mo picks up before I answer.

"Hang up, mom!"

"I don't know what you boys are up to. I don't even wanna know!"

The morning wasn't beaming like a normal race day. It rained overnight, and although there's a soothing smell from the green grass, it's cold and puddles line the path.

"Bro, I didn't come out here just to get my Jordans wet." Mo said with concern.

"Just avoid the puddles bro, it'll be alright."

We line up with the other runners. Starting lines like these are always tricky. Maneuvering away from long-legged adults takes practice. Everyone is out for themselves when the gunshot sounds. There's a moment of stillness before the fray . . .

"POP!"

Bodies scatter and legs are fusion. Two hundred legs churn asphalt with rubber soles. Elbows are sharp-edged. Heads bop up and down. The race is liquid with runners flowing toward the end. To my surprise Mo starts in a sprint. I'm worried because in all my plotting and conniving, I forgot to go over a game plan with him about the race. I'm running at a faster pace than I want to trying to keep Mo in sight. Sure, I want to beat him, but I want a fair match. I already know the outcome of his sprint; he is surely to burn out after a mile or so, I've done the same thing myself. I eventually lose sight of Mo and slow my pace a bit. I figure I'll make a push for him around the second mile if I don't catch him by then. As soon as I establish my game plan, I see Mo slouched over on the side of the path trying to catch his breath.

Mo and I idle dangerously within this human wind tunnel. Surely an adult running at top speed could trample us, but Mo's patented jab-steps come in handy as we both dodge a human train wreck. Stooped in safety, Mo states the obvious:

"I think I started off too fast."

"It happens bro, I did the same thing in my first race."

"Why didn't you warn me, man?!!" (Still gagging.)

In my mind I thought about running in place but decided

against it, for it would be too callous. I still had a desire to finish strong in the race. My plan to beat Mo not only backfired, but now he's in uncharted territory with me as his only friend. It is time for me to show compassion. A time to be the friend to Mo that he had been to me. A time to put my arm around him and say, "Let's finish this race together."

Instead, I give running tips to Mo, telling him to put his hands on his head and start walking, that this would open up his lungs and help him recover quickly. Then I point to a makeshift water station just around the bend.

"Walk there, get some water and start running at slow pace again. If you feel you can't make it start walking again and put your hands on your head."

"Cool."

"I'm gonna take off, bro."

"Go ahead, I'll be alright."

So I left. And didn't turn back around. Earlier I counted a total of seven kids that looked like they were under 14 and that included Mo and I. As I sprinted back to the head of the pack, I felt I still had a good chance at winning the 14 and under category. I passed any kid in sight until only adults were in front of me. Finishing the race with Mo would've been the right thing, though, and I know my parents would've been so proud of me. Yet in my own mind I project the thought that my parents would be prouder of me winning the race.

I cross the line and a man with a clipboard writes down my bib number. Then I see my parents.

"Where's Geranimo?" asks Dad.

"I had to pass him at the first bend. He was really winded, but he started running again. I bet he'll be here soon."

As we wait for Mo to finish, I think about what I did. Mo never left me behind. Never. He even intervened on my behalf before Pablo pummeled me for touching a stack of tortillas.

We eventually see Mo come into view. He's walking again

with his hands on his head. When he sees us near the finish line he starts running again. Mo doesn't sprint this time, he jogs with that same cool jog he has after scoring a basket against one of his opponents.

The last batch of runners come in shortly after Mo finishes the race, and as storm clouds begin to rumble, there's a push to rush the awards ceremony. Everyone gathers by the statue next to the parking lot. Most of the major players are already in the winner's circle. The adult male and female runners for 1st, 2nd and 3rd place claim their respective spots. Next is the 14 and under category. I see the man with the clipboard again and he points at me to come up. As I walk to the winner's circle a woman shouts, "No! *This* (pointing to Mo) is the young man who crossed the finish line first!"

The man with the clipboard intervenes.

"No, ma'am, this young man is the winner, I took his number down when he crossed . . . "

"But I saw with my own two eyes that this young man was first!" escorting Mo to the winner's circle as well.

In the woman's defense, it must not have been too hard to mix us up, two brown boys around the same height. My parents are silent through the kerfuffle, chomping at the bit to leave as they stand in the cold. The woman is sure of what she saw, and Mo and I are too tired to argue with these psycho adults anyway. Storm clouds keep brewing. Finally, another man from what must've been the council stated abruptly, "Since we don't know which of these young men crossed the line first, we'll give 'em both 2nd place medals," ending the feud and moving the already awkward ceremony along.

On the ride home I think about the predicament I put Mo in. Mo is never mean, he just happens to be extremely talented at the sport of basketball, surely, I could deal with being third in a strong trifecta. Mo is supremely confident but believing in yourself is not a crime. Hey, even I feel better about myself when I'm around him. Mo is the best friend a kid could have, and I basically played him to try and beat him at a sport he was unfamiliar with.

We round the corner to Mo's block then into the alley. I desperately want to be the winner of the spoils, so I tell Mo, "You competed hard today, brother, but I had to win the race."

"I won, too." Mo replies, holding up his medal.

"See, I won 2nd Place!"

COME CLEAN

I WAKE UP TO THE SOUND of Mo vomiting in the bathroom. His laborious belching is quickly drowned out by Cathy's yells. As I piece together the previous night, I realize Mo's body is rejecting the pills. Wait, *what is Cathy sayin'?!* She keeps on about Carla's stomach having to be pumped. For sure this isn't an opportunity to parade around innocently but I know I must emerge from the basement and risk getting caught in the crossfire. Sibling rivalry aside, this isn't the time for that, and I know it. What occurs to me though—and what I can do however, is try to distract Cathy from her own barrage. Hovering over the porcelain Mo is defenseless saying, "I know, Ma, I know!" praying that his mom will leave him be so he can do his business in peace. No, Cathy's too smart for that, seizing this moment to make Mo suffer more than he already is in order to teach him about the ills of drugs. She posts up at the bathroom door, bending down to yell in his ear, amplifying her pleas point blank range into his cranium. While exercising her solar plexus at Mo's behest, I sneak by to make my way to the big-pin cushioned seat. But Cathy shoots me a question so fierce that my breath leaves my body.

"Did you take them pills, too?!!"

"No, Cathy."

" . . . SEE MO, YOU GOTTA FOLLOW THE EXAMPLE OF YOUR FRIEND!"

Of course, the shit backfires. And right now, I know that I can't bail him out. He's going to have to take whatever comes spewing out of Cathy's mouth until she gets tired. I chime in every now and then to give Mo temporary relief, distraction as it were, asking stupid questions like, "What hospital is she at?" and "How long is she gonna be there?" Mo finally comes out of the bathroom wiping his mouth and chin with a wash rag. Cathy then explains to us the intricacies of Carla's treatment . . .

It started with a dare. Mo was excited to introduce me to his cousin, Carla. She was 17, stood a good foot over me and Mo and her short hair accentuated her long nose which was shaped like a ski slope. She had plain gold-hoop earrings and an army green coat, seemed extremely comfortable in her own skin and talked like one of the guys. The night was full of her and Mo trying to one-up each other. At this I had to watch because for one, I'd never seen Mo this hype on a person before and two, I knew she would give him a serious run for his money.

NoDoz is no joke, but what are nothing but caffeine pills we treat as something taboo. And we miss the part about them making you sick if you take too many. Nausea, vomiting, not to mention hospitalization. Since none of us is running fever, breaking the cap's seal is like breaking the law. We upended the childproof top, then punctured its silver lining and fished out the cotton. Carla shook the bottle, and we heard the condensed rain sound of those beautiful white pills clacking against the white plastic. We're grown, and there's no need to worry, Carla was our adult supervision. Who's going to stay more awake and watch scary movies all night? We needed medicine.

The pills were tiny. Five of them could fit on your fingertip. Carla starts with two, then doubles-back saying, "Oh shit! I better read the Directions label," as if the Directions would be able to reverse an overdose. Mo chuckles at Carla's pompous attitude and I watch earnestly, curious at what will transpire but confused at what game this was and how one could win. After Mo swallowed three No Doz with the help of a 7Up, I waved the white flag preemptively. Didn't know the game and didn't wanna know either. "Good, you won't waste our time, then," Carla said, clearly dissing me but that diss sounded good flowing from her lips. She was a renegade, a fashionista no doubt but that diss—however brief—made me blush for a sec. The "Say No to Drugs" campaign is everywhere right now but pills? Pills aren't drugs. Shit, you buy No Doz in Safeway, right? They don't sell drugs in Safeway. But that was neither here nor there, Carla was up to five No Doz as she swallowed another three. Looking back, I don't know what we thought would happen. I mean, they wouldn't realize its affects until early morning because we stood up to 2am any-fuckin'-way.

Earlier that night, Cathy was neither impressed nor disenchanted by Carla. Although Carla looked like a full-grown woman to us, Cathy saw right through her. Still, she didn't judge Carla for hangin' around with two twelve-year-olds at her age and must have trusted her, for she was family.

Mo must've figured these miniscule pills a waste of time, upheaved ten more, placed them on his tongue and took the 7Up to the head again.

"That's thirteen!" Mo said to Carla, slamming the 7Up can down on his dresser.

"Unlucky number thirteen." I stated begrudgingly from the sidelines.

It wasn't a dare, just an observation I made, hoping for the best but fearing the worst. Without saying a word Mo went back into the bottle, retrieving three more white dots and swallowed 'em.

"Sixteen." Aiming his proclamation at me this time.

Carla—not to be outdone—and desperately trying to take Mo's attention from me, lit up a whole handful.

"Fuck keeping track," she spouted, "keeping track is for sissies."

Peer pressure is a muthafucker. But Carla and Mo didn't make me do anything I didn't want to do. Deep down they were just challenging each other. Underneath all the layers of Carla's intricate persona, she admired Mo. It was also apparent that Mo admired Carla. So what was the competition about? Did he want to prove to his cousin that he could hang? And besides that, where was her judgement? Someone had to be the older one. I witnessed Mo's competitiveness get the best of him that night. Just as I witnessed Carla's unflatteringly tumultuous urge to be liked. But I also witnessed the wisdom and fairness of Cathy the following day, when she had to show tough love to Mo. Hovering over the toilet, she used me as an example to Mo of how to stay out of the shit. It's groundbreaking but hard to do, parents willing to admit when their kids are wrong, much less telling 'em they need to follow the example of a friend.

Cathy continued . . .

"HOW MANY PILLS DID YOU TAKE, MO?!"

"16."

"SIXTEEN!!"

Carla was never invited back. And it was the end of any flirtatious feelings Mo would have toward a drug. From then on, he was a straight shooter.

RESTIN' ON THEM 7'S

LET'S TAKE A TRIP BACK to Mo's beginning for a sec. To 1977, the Year of the Snake. Santana releases *Festival*, and its album cover dons two symbiotic and symmetrical snakes on a bed of rose petals coalescing from a Dragon's snout. '76 is the Yang Dragon, '77 the Yin Snake. Both contain the Fire Element. Cosmological syzygies of the highest order. Those born in '77 are debonair, one day tipping the scales for afternoon lovemaking, confidence, and consciousness. The world becomes a collage. A contract on the world love jam. Musically and spiritually, Santana proclaims, "Let the Children Play." It is a sermon to the Earth and open areas. In inner cities new asphalt is poured and smoothed, running surfaces. White lines are curved and edged, cosmic play. The arrival of a transformational year is here. A new epoch. Geometrical shades of sunlight cast upon 365 stairs. The coming of those who will remind us that the world is Maya. Vibrations are abound . . .

Although Mo's birth would be celebrated by the cosmos, his conception was a thousand times more complicated, for he was completely unaware of the secrecy he idled in. A prominent man in Cathy's community, a leader, a trustworthy man on the surface, was acting wickedly behind the scenes. He molested Cathy—she was sixteen. He saw her in the neighborhood and—

He forced his weight on top of her. Pinning her down. Her nose smooshed against the light stubble of his cheeks while Cathy took in that awful smell of his cologne: Old Spice. Later, one whiff of the stuff would be enough to make her vomit. He slumped over her, told her to calm down, assured her things would be okay. But as soon as she told him—expecting—he grabbed her arm and squeezed, shook her hard then ultimately, let go. His body slouched, head and eyes dropping to the ground until he raised his left hand to glance upon his own wedding ring. Happily married, but now a hesitant father by way of an illicit affair. He found her so unbelievably beautiful, the whole world in her eyes, containing all the blessings for a peaceful Earth. She is passionate, walking with power and grace, long black hair and succulent lips. What he found so prevalent in Cathy, that youthful grace she exuded in her walk, made him so erratic that he burgeoned into predatory behavior. Before, he never had the courage to face his own demons but now a child would be proof of an uncontrollable urge. "What would Regina say?" he thought. But in the next millisecond he reasoned with himself: "I just can't tell her; I'll keep it a secret . . . "

Sure. Simple. Always a man thinking about himself. He couldn't risk the ridicule, the shame, the ostracization. Only he and Cathy knew. And he knew that she would not risk her own ostracization, though it would happen naturally in society. A part of Cathy was glad it was over. He never said a word one way or another, but after she told him she was pregnant she knew that he would never push himself onto her again.

NEVER NO TIME TO PLAY. The only thing Cathy knows is to love her child from the outset. She ventures to the library looking for some good reads and checks out a book on Geronimo, the Chiricahua Apache leader. Throughout the book's pages, Geronimo's words give her strength through this uncharted terrain. It's a monumental story. A story for his people—for all people—and for the child growing inside of her, regardless of circumstances, a blessing from the Creator in the form of this life force.

Cathy grew up on the East Side of Denver. As a student at Mitchell Elementary School, she hadn't even crossed the Platte River before she was transported back to her own ancestral roots. When Cathy was in the 6th grade, she joined the Crusade for Justice. It's fitting that Geronimo's book was the one she sought out. It was a pursuit of nourishment for her soul—for her baby's soul—which partly stemmed from the school's proudly indigenous and self-sufficient narrative. There—at Escuela—she learned the power of protest. And now, retrospectively, her son's very life and existence will be proof of a protest over wickedness, as well as an attestation of love conquering all. Cathy's quest for these nine months was to rejuvenate her spirit, body and environment.

When shame rose to the surface of Cathy's being, she quelled it with forgiveness and love. Forgiving herself was difficult to muster, but when looking at life through the wonderment of motherhood, it had to be done, she would have to move on; to be a clean slate as soon as her son's eyes gleamed upon her. Hiding underneath a sheath of guilt was love and enlightenment. Even with her son growing inside her she kept guilt at bay from tainting the energy of new life.

The Voyager probes are launched from Earth. The Milky Way—as predicted by the Mayans—approaches the elliptical plane of the universe. Newspapers promote astrolatry on page 45. Constellations wait in vain for atoms on our planet to self-actualize. People are killed for fossil fuels as water-powered carburetors are shelved by corporations. Vibrations are abound. The uroboros is a phonographic plate on a direct-drive turntable. A pregnant mother walks into a storefront. Denver, Colorado.

Vibrations are abound at 45 rpm. Cathy is home alone on a

chilly October evening. The day before found her at Jerry's Record Shop at 1515 Broadway with her girlfriend, Angie, picking up the new Earth, Wind & Fire song, "Serpentine Fire," which has steadily slid up the charts. Back at home she walks over to the turntable and drops the needle, sitting down with a warm cup of tea, covering herself with a serape. Her pregnant belly protrudes from the colorful patterns and she caresses her son with circular motions. The album drops in a couple weeks and Cathy will soon scan every centimeter of the album's cover. Japanese artist Shusei Nagaoka will capture Maurice White's love of Egyptology perfectly, and the artwork will remind Cathy of Corky's speeches, his love for Teotihuacán and the Pyramid of the Sun. Yet the lyrics emanating from the 45 tell a different story . . . from the East. The Kundalini. Spinal fluid and the spine's resemblance to a serpent, and its fire—Kundalini awakened. Music is not only entertaining but attaining. Songs of reverence and belief are abound. The vibrations influence all soundwaves in its circumference, painting luscious patterns upon DNA. Cathy's hip to it, her baby kicks to it, and all the world is a stage.

The musical montage of Cathy's pregnancy parallels the book on Geronimo and the influences become Mo's medley. She nears the birth, and by now her attacker's hands are a distant memory. Cathy's attention and awareness grasp onto Geronimo's words and her mind is set. Her son will have to persevere from the jump. She will educate and nurture him. Nothing will be lacking. Despite his origin, the destination is clear. It was written in stone before the flesh was formed, and the fight for indigenous rights rages on.

Fishscale. October 1977. Uncle Slam is again pulling white rabbits out of thin air. More treaties are broken. This time in the Pacific North-west. Fish are mounted for sport and sportsmen are appalled by indigenous people hunting fish for food. Liberty's scales tip toward a coup. Besieged by lures, bait and Congressional double talk, lands are seized. Another win for the oligarchs. The law of the high seas, otherwise

REMINDING ME OF MO

known as *Maritime Admiralty Law, is weaponized against tribal sovereignty. Captains pronounce trophy fish as cargo and proceed to prey
upon seas, lakes and rivers. But the Creator is at work, simultaneously
birthing children whilst conjuring a blue star. The dream of the planet.
Destined to break free from life's wheel. Trapped in three-dimensions
yet tearing through the veil. Muddled by senses but clearing the void.
The intrinsic path pointing toward the stars. The first Kachina doll with
a basketball. The here now. Cohesion.*

MO IS BORN WITH ROLLER SKATES on his feet as DJ's
across the country spin epic orange labels at 33 1/3. The rain,
shine, won't mind, and a brief heatwave melts Denver snow. The
date is October 30, 1977. Mo is jump stop on blacktop energy.
Inquisitive. Charming. Charismatic. And one thing he has from
the jump: Belief. All is good and it's time to go. He dives, swims
and eventually, flows. Like a bird on the wing. Mo arrives in late
1977 but isn't late to the party. He understands the meaning of
Godspeed, and prepares himself, and the rest of the world, for his
journey. The universe places 7 upon him. Just like Mo's birth
year: Restin' on them 7's. God Power. Cathy looks down upon
her newborn son, Geranimo Antonio Maestas, born to persevere.
The rejuvenation of her soul is complete. And Mo's energy—his
ferromagnetism—begins.

ONE TO GROW ON

WHEN WE MEET JERRY MEDINA he looks like a poser. I don't even know what that word means but at one look we know Jerry is an odd kid. His hair is frosted blonde only in the front and it mimics some type of squirrel hat. His t-shirt collar is stretched out sloppily and his chin just kind of melts away into his neck. Add braces to the mix and there you have the oddest kid in the bunch, especially when you factor that most of the school is in Z. Cavaricci's and British Knights. Jerry sported Vans when the whole of our neighborhood had never even seen a skateboard before. Despite these oddities, Jerry has a strong sense of self as evidenced by his wears. He walks around as if the rest of us are missing out on something that only Jerry knows. Sure, we've heard of skateboarding, but we know nothing about the culture.

In the classroom, Jerry is far from a teacher's pet, often tiptoeing between insubordinations and becoming the model student. Plus he has an ace up his sleeve, Jerry's mother is a big-to-do in the upper echelon of the DPS School Board, which means that Jerry is unfuckwittable. He gives teachers all the rope they need to hang themselves. As soon as they scolded Jerry for his crass behavior, Principal John Sanchez was there to slap a muzzle on the teacher so fast, they never even knew what hit 'em. Most times it was worse, and rumors went that Principal Sanchez would not only muzzle a teacher, but have 'em sit there while Jerry's mother would spout her angst of needing to drive from downtown to punish some juvenile teacher.

But Jerry's mom can't protect him when he's out of the classroom. Out of the classroom, he was fair game and Mo knew it. Jerry bumped Guns N' Roses instead of Kid N' Play. But Mo embraced Jerry's oddities.

"Where you from?" Asked Mo.

"I live up by Berkeley Park," said Jerry.

"So you take the bus too?"

"Sometimes I ride the bus, sometimes my mom drops me off on her way to work."

"Where does she work?"

"Downtown."

"Isn't that out the way?"

"She doesn't mind."

"You hoop?"

"Yeah, but usually I do hacky sack."

"Huh?"

[Jerry breaks out a hacky sack from his backpack.]

"YO, WHAT THE HELL IS THAT?!!"

"It's a hacky sack. You've never seen a hacky sack before?"

"What do you do with it?"

"You just kick it around, here, let me show you."

"What's in it?"

"Rice."

"Oh."

"It's not gonna get my Jordans dirty, right?"

"It won't."

"You sure?"

"It won't. Honest. My mom'll buy you a new pair of Jordans if it does."

"—Can your mom buy me a new pair of shoes, too?" Chimes Pablo, making Mo smile.

"No, but she can buy you a short-sleeved shirt to go along with those shorts, though."

"Ooooooh shit!" That got Mo laughing, and he slaps fives with Jerry.

I didn't say a word and didn't laugh, I knew if I did, Pablo would be waiting for me later. Jerry commenced to kicking and we all picked it up nicely. By the next Monday, damn near everybody on 826 had a hacky sack and could do about 3-4 kicks. Shirley confiscated three of them before we even boarded the bus. Oh, we played ball, too, trust me, but Mo quickly made mention of Jerry's odd shooting posture which was due to his left-handedness.

"—I don't even wanna swat your shot cause it looks too fucked up to begin with." Pablo threatened, then subsequently swatted Jerry's shot anyway.

There were times when we ignored Jerry and he would try to foray into the circumference of another crew, for his oddities could only be absorbed in small doses. As far as I was concerned, we had our trio. If it ain't broke, don't fix it. But Mo wasn't born with that type of close-mindedness. He was curious about people and willing to understand what made them tick. Mo believed the more the merrier, and everyone brings something to the table. Case in point Jerry's hacky sack, and attitude, and his awkward left-handedness. I knew Jerry desired to be cool, and nothing was cooler than being down with Mo. So Jerry didn't mind being the butt of our jokes, if only for a little while.

MONTBELLO

SCHOOL IS DONE IN THE middle of 1990 and we're ready for another great summer. Then we get hit with a bomb. Mo's family is moving to Montbello. It's quick and sudden. It's like I blinked, and Mo was gone. Before Mo and I were friends, I kicked it with Filberto Fernandez, who lives three houses down from me. When Mo blessed me into his circle, I thought being confined to Quivas Street was a thing of the past, and I walked on the opposite side of the block of Berto's house en route to Mo's. Yet Mo moved away, and he wasn't coming back. I had dissed Berto and left him hangin', a fact I didn't realize—or own up to—until Mo was gone. So I did what any kid would have done, I took my lumps and apologized. And as expected, without Mo around, Pablo and I fell out of contact with each other.

A couple months had passed. One afternoon found Berto and I listening to Stone Cold Rhymin' by Young M.C. on the tape deck of my dad's work truck. My mom emerged from the house in the middle of "I Come Off" and motioned the phone gesture to me.

"I'll be right back, bro."

"Cool."

Walking into house I was curious of who was on the phone because I was already with Berto.

"Hello."

"Gabe, what's up, man?!"

"Mo?!"

"Yeah. What you up to?"

"Nothin', just hangin' out," careful not to mention Berto as if Mo would be mad or something.

"Hey man, you should come up to our new house in Montbello and spend the weekend up here. Me and my mom can pick you up."

"Is it cool?"

"Cool?! What you worried about?! Of course it's cool, no one's gonna bother us on the block, everyone's chill. We'll just hang out, maybe play some ball, all that."

"Alright, sounds good, let me ask my mom."

My mom asked where Mo lived now and how I would get there. I told her he lived on the East Side, (I didn't know where the hell Montbello was) and that he and Cathy would pick me up. She said yes while trying to play up her concern, but I knew it was a relief. With four kids in the house during summer, doing without one for a weekend was somewhat of a break. I didn't know anything about Montbello but regardless, I would've followed Mo to Compton.

I returned to my dad's work truck. Berto had the volume cranked on Stone Cold Rhymin'. He turned it down as I slid into the cab.

"Who was it?"

"Geranimo."

"Oh," said Berto, holding a pause that felt like minutes. We didn't say much during the next song, but Berto left when we saw a Pizza Pro's delivery driver descend down the block and stop in front of his house.

"Aww yeah! See ya later, bro."

"You're lucky, man."

* * *

To re-up can mean any number of things. The term has been around before our parents' parents were born. It has survived many generations and still basically means the same thing. Over the years we've added to it. Meanings and actions and duties and legend. Sometimes the re-up is a two-part action. First, the promise: hey, man, I'll re-up with you in a minute. Then, the action, you actually re-up with homie. Sounds easy, right? Not so fast. Contained within those tiny four letters split two by two is a world of commitment, promise and action. If your word is bond you better re-up, and if you re-up, your word is bond.

It's not like I didn't witness Mo refining relationships. During our time together he dragged me from St. Charles to the East Side to Swansea and back. Along the way he remembered names, faces, your strengths, your weaknesses. He lit up Ray Ray's day like a toy hidden deep in a cereal box, and he respected his sister Lala's privacy, having the wherewithal to never invade her room unless invited in.

I have no idea of what's in store, I only know that Mo is a good host and never short on the list of things to do. He always anticipates his next move and isn't the type to tell his mom he's bored. On the contrary, if he feels even the inkling of boredom, he is quick to venture outside and spark up a convo with someone. That's the real-deal Holyfield. He won't watch no TV sitcoms, he's more down to explore the world, just two feet and a pristine pair of Jordans.

I pack my clothes for Mo's house and think about his penchant for making homemade Rice Krispie treats. We used to think Kellog's might mass-produce these joints one day, but we appreciate that they print a simple recipe right on the box. I for sure can't make 'em, and in Mo's absence—when I tried to do the same on my mom's stove—I almost burnt the house down, ruining one of my mom's pans and causing my dad to open every window in the house to get the smoke out. It wasn't as easy as Mo made it look, and I secretly hoped he would make 'em again so I could see it one more time and then maybe I could trust myself on the stove again. Maybe it was the all-white spatula that he glided back and forth—somewhat poetically—evening out the warm treats over a waxed cookie sheet. Or maybe it was confidence.

I'm waiting on my porch when Mo and Cathy pull up in a brown Suburu hatchback. I heap my backpack onto my shoulder and slide into the back seat.

"How ya doin', mijo?" Cathy says.

"Good!" I respond, just as Mo swivels around in the passenger seat, extending his arm out with a closed fist. That quick and simple dap let me know from jump that the only thing lost between Mo and I is time. All we have to do now is kick back and enjoy the ride. We drive east down I-70 and Cathy has an air about her. It feels as though she had graduated from the North Side to greener pastures and is driving Mo and I to some type of retreat. She is happy and soulful, and in her was a sense of the saying, "No matter where you go, there you are." Her mood is infectious—it always was—and as the prelude to our reunion it's the equivalent of a cracked champagne glass onto a ship's hull.

Mo is unusually low-key despite Cathy's gregarious mood. Those two share a tight bond so it's odd Mo's not on cloud nine with his mom. When Cathy asks us what we have in store for the weekend, Mo redirects his mom's question to the flowing traffic and the timed bumps in the road as we pass the Purina Dog Food factory. Right then it's clear to me what Mo is doing. He has plans for all types of shit for us to do but he doesn't want Cathy knowing about any of it. After realizing Mo is using silence to conceal his devious intentions, my anticipation for the weekend increased, slightly eased by the swooshing of the summer breeze.

When we arrive at Mo's house, he turns around to tell me the mission.

"First things first," Mo says, "we have to head to Fuquan's."

Fuquan's house is smack dab in the middle of the cul-de-sac holding together the block and my mind trys to grasp the fact that there were no alleys or thoroughfares as we walk; it's the first time I've ever seen one. Nobody answers after Mo rings the doorbell and after two knocks, he pushes his way in. He looks back at me from inside the house with a convincing smile and motions with his head for me to follow. I refuse to move.

"It's summer break, man, there ain't no parents at home." Mo states as a matter of fact.

He does have a point. Plus, I would rather be mischievous with Mo than be by myself on an unknown block.

We enter the house and convene at the top of a staircase descending into the basement. I follow Mo down the blue carpeted stairs as he explains some type of search and rescue mission.

"I know he's down here," Mo says in a tone that sounds similar to a parent about to scold someone, "We gotta dig him out!"

We enter a room to the right of the stairs and hear, "Whadup Mo?!"

"Mo!!"

"Whadup playboi!!!"

"Awww shit!!"

Mo introduces me to the guys that greeted him. Carlos, Dante, Valdo and Joe. Carlos is at a desk fidgeting with a Styrofoam airplane while Dante chills on an oversized bean bag. Valdo thumbs through a Playboy and Joe—the youngest of the bunch—cheers on Quan's character as the hero in Nintendo's *Metroid*.

When Mo finally introduces me to Quan, the brother unglues his eyes from the TV for a quick glance in my direction and a subsequent nod. By the time I reciprocate the nod, Quan's eyes are already back on his game. Mo then asks Quan what he has on the menu for the day and Quan ignores him. Mo seems unaffected by Quan's dismissal and I'm trying to pick up on any tension between Mo and Quan but there doesn't seem to be any. Quan ignoring Mo now looks more like a sibling rivalry rather than a legitimate beef. Nevertheless, Mo goes in:

"What'cha gonna do Quan? Stay in and play video games all day?"

Not only does Quan refuse to acknowledge Mo's questions, he ramps up the intensity of how he's slapping the buttons on his controller.

Mo then tries a consensus by floating an idea through the room.

"Let's all go play some ball guys. Y'all don't want to stay down here forever, right?"

But the only sound is Fuquan's fidgety fingers atop the controller while the guys hold tight, careful not to make a move or add input without Quan's approval, knowing that Mo is subtly challenging Quan's influence over the group.

Mo doesn't have a Nintendo. He used to ride his bike to his uncle's house to play. He likes playing it but no cartridge could overtake the divinity of that round orange ball.

We continue watching Fuquan attempt to beat a death-defying level, only to crash and burn over and over again at the same juncture. I appreciate the homie's persistence but it's clear that something has to give. It's also clear that Quan lives for video games, for his basement room replete with wood paneling is a gaming paradise, it's completely disconnected from the outside world, not to mention sunshine.

Sunshine is what Mo is advocating for. And to relieve the rest of us from Quan's inevitable 16-bit fate, Mo finally says, "Let me give it a shot, Quan." This time Quan is visibly agitated, squirming hastily in his chair and scoffing at Mo's offer to help. Mo even tries the Obi-Won Kenobi inside-your-head Force speech: "Quan . . . brother . . . it's time." There's so much pushing that I'm contemplating telling Mo to ease up a bit because when Quan stands up to stretch, he is at least a foot taller than Mo. Thankfully, things don't pop off but the others in the room are swayed by Mo's campaigning and start chiming in too, even they know it's only a matter of time before we're entrenched in a mean game of 21. That's when Quan throws the controller down and yells, "Alright, fuck it! Let's go!"

Mo doesn't claim victory quite yet. Knowing Quan is still frustrated from both the game and his pestering, Mo lightens the mood by tossing Quan the basketball so he can dribble as we mob to the court, playfully jabbing his side. It isn't a long walk to the park, and I see in Fuquan's eyes that he wants to crush Mo. I'm curious of what will transpire in this upcoming battle, one I think Mo might lose based on Quan's height and motivation.

The improvements I thought I'd made in my game mean nothing this afternoon. I'm again relegated to watching two behemoths of the basketball court just as I had a year earlier when Mo and Pablo would fight for the crown. Fuquan has a turnaround jumper that Mo can't contest, so he goes to it frequently. As the game intensifies Quan uses it every time. He isn't talking much and to my surprise, Mo isn't either. Mo not taunting someone on the court is extremely rare, but Quan's jumpers are taking their toll. I'm thinking Mo realizes that he'll have to outscore Quan instead of exhausting all his energy on defense. I can't argue with Mo's strategy. Besides, he's already built up his score twice, because when he reached a total of 16, Quan one-hand tipped him down to zero. Mo rallies back to a point total of 15 but Quan reaches the line with 20, needing only one top-of-the-key shot to win. The shot seems long when the ball is in the air and the rest of us crash the lane, scurrying for a long rebound . . . but it banks in.

"Game." claims Fuquan in a relieved tone, quickly adding, "I'm done y'all."

"You didn't even call bank Quan." Mo says plainly. Which really, he didn't.

It was an ugly shot, but the game winner nonetheless, and we all suspect that Quan knows he escaped one. Mo scored twice as many points and was finding his groove. Yet Quan isn't taking the bait about not calling bank as he did when Mo pestered him out of the basement. Quan realizes the rematch will be Mo's game, but rather than pushing Quan like he did before, Mo looks at Quan's no eye-contact exit and knows his rematch will have to wait for at least another day. "Thanks for playin', Quan," Mo says as Quan walks away. And without turning around Quan lifts his arm in acknowledgement of Mo's statement and keeps walking. The others follow single file until it's just Mo and I on the court. The demeanor of Quan's exit ensured that he could play Nintendo for the rest of the day in his gaming paradise with wood paneling without so much as a whisper from Mo. But if I know Mo, I know we'll end up right back at Quan's tomorrow.

When we return to Mo's he heads straight to his room, pops a tape into the deck and walks out. I hear the tub spout turn on in the bathroom down the hall when the bass drops to Ice Cube's "Who's the Mack?" I then hear, "Gabe!" over the full blast of the stereo. I venture into the hallway and see Mo's Air Jordans and socks laying just outside of the entrance to the bathroom. I glance in and find Mo sitting on the edge of the bathtub soaking his feet in talcum powder. When Mo lived on Pecos Street, Cathy consistently made him douse his feet in talcum powder when we came in from playing basketball. This time however, Mo went straight for the talcum powder without his mom uttering a word, in fact she's not even here, for she would definitely be against Mo shaking all the walls in the house with his sound system. I put the lid down on the toilet and cop a seat, wondering if Mo had grown tired of his mom pressing him all the time about washing his feet or if he somehow got used to the relaxation of the running water and adopted it as his new postgame ritual. Nevertheless, Hip Hop and talcum powder provide normalcy and although Mo lost the game, he wielded the most influence on the block despite being younger and shorter than Quan. Mo's a mover and a shaker, he can convince the sun to shine brighter if he wants to.

Mo's room is the ultimate cool-out-pad. It has the shape of an A with the two walls of the ceiling making a point in the middle. Upon each descending wall Mo has posters of Jordan pinned up so at all times he would be mid-flight looking down on you. A single window stands at the opposite end of the entrance and the walls are painted a manly blueish gray. Mo's sophisticated sound system runs alongside one wall while his bed laces the other.

The next day is more of the same. Parading to Fuquan's to dig him out again. Basketball games of 21 with Mo exacting his revenge and letting Quan have every word of it on the way back. But midday Mo changes course from the usual and takes me to the rooftop. We exit the top floor window of his room and sit high above those long-necked houses. From that height we witness a profound view of the Denver Metropolitan area and take in the sights with not many words. This is as serene and introspective as I have ever seen Mo, he is growing into a well-rounded young man. The minutes feel like hours and the scenery nourishes our budding spirituality. All we know is that it's summertime and we are living and breathing in the moment, taking nothing for granted.

* * *

WE SIT ON THE LIVING ROOM COUCH as I look up at the vaulted ceiling—another anomaly I'd never seen. Mo has his feet up on the coffee table and is again fielding questions from Cathy, who's busy making dinner in the kitchen. Mo disposes of her questions in one-word answers just as he did before but instead of trying to hide his intent, his disposal of these inquiries seem to stem from simply desiring some relaxation. He knows his mom is trying to make us both feel comfortable when in actuality, we're as relaxed as family can be. I marvel at the white walls descending from the roof and how the skylight accentuates the mysterious night—the staircase a mere indentation of empty space. I glance into the kitchen and witness steam emanating from a huge pot on the stove. When Cathy sees that I'm interested in the steam she asked, "You ever had cabbage, mijo?"

"No, Cathy."

"Well you're in for a treat, mijo! I'm making cabbage and beef."

I want Mo to chime in on the dish, but his eyes are focused on the TV. It doesn't matter what Cathy puts in front of him, he's going to eat and eat good. I make up my mind that I'm going to eat whatever is in front of me too. Cathy was always a gracious host and I know Mo won't stand for my picky eating habits. In the end it doesn't matter. Cathy's love for us and her support of our friendship—despite our geographic differences—embody the dish. I discover my love for cabbage and ask for seconds. Cathy also lets us eat in front of the TV, so here we sit, like we used to on the big-pinned cushion seats.

The following day it was time to go home. Mo asks me to stay one more day but I decline for the simple fact I'm out of clean clothes. That's the only reason I didn't stay longer. Mo even offers up the washer and dryer so I can clean my clothes there, but to that point my mom had always done my laundry so I don't have a clue on how to operate a washing machine, though I can't let Mo know it, he'll definitely let me have it on that one.

During the ride home I'm extremely grateful that Mo exhumed me from the North Side for a minute. My whole world is there, as opposed to Mo who seems to hopscotch over the Denver Metropolitan area as if he had painted the lines himself. Mo loves Denver. East, North, West or South. Montbello, Swansea, Sunnyside or Downtown. From any Recreation Center, YMCA or school gym to any nook and cranny basketball court in the city. It doesn't matter if it has chain nets or white, he's there. Disneyland? Disneyland is at 38th & Tennyson. But my homie Mo is teaching me that there's a broader city right around the corner.

As we drive down Pecos Street and pass Remington Elementary, Mo and I promise each other that we'll get together more often, whether that means that he'll come to the North Side or that I'll venture out to the Bellows again. The foundation is set, and the plan is to keep in touch well into our high school years.

Promises are always the same—full of promise. In the middle of Quivas Street—as we clutch our brown hands together in a sign of solidarity—we say our goodbyes and I walk into the house, grateful for Mo's friendship.

PORTRAIT OF THE MIDDLE SCHOOLER AS A HOOD

IF GANGS DON'T RECRUIT YOU, it'll be the DPD, because the Denver Police Department has the upper hand as far as entry into the Denver Public Schools are concerned. Streets are dangerous. Gangsta rap is on the rise. Control slips form the grips of the state and anarchy flourishes. Police can't find the cause. They blinked their eyes one day and gangs were everywhere. (Is how they tell it.) To attempt to minimize crime in all districts they turn to recruitment. "Get 'em young," was their motto. They realized younger siblings had older brothers and sisters who were affiliated, and to the DPD, affiliated meant lost cause. Better to grind out the war in budding classrooms because this proud group will never revert back from reppin' their colors. The Denver Police Department began visiting schools that had seen upticks in violence and violent crimes, where teachers had witnessed horrific initiation practices, and where roll call in a classroom could mean one less pupil. For the day, for the semester, forever.

Mo is in seventh grade and back on the East Side of Denver. At the same time he and his peers turn in parent consent forms to learn sex education, they also learn—courtesy of the Denver

Police Department (and without a parent consent form)—all about gang culture. Topics they'll cover include how to identify gang members through dress, tattoos, signs and speech, what to do if you encounter a gang member, like calling an anti-gang hotline, as well as initiation rituals and the psychology of gangs. These topics parallel sex education fundamentals of male and female genitalia, the taboo discussion of masturbation, and a scientific approach to intercourse. Thus, in the fall of 1991, Mo and his peers learn both how to create life, and how it could be taken.

A Nova special is shown of a man ejaculating inside of a woman, the deep-voiced narrator documenting the sperm's journey to the fallopian tube. Sperm die faster than rival gangstas on the street, but the remaining sperm keep moving. Of course the woman and man don't have names, this is science for Pete's sake, as if the insides of their bodies are devoid of soul. At the pinnacle, a single sperm enters the egg and the miracle of life is created. Its entry into the egg is an initiation of sorts, and they learn that from the beginning, initiations are a part of life. After lunch they receive a new type of initiation, though nothing about this particular initiation is miraculous. It is cataclysmic, woeful and of dire consequence.

Officers Montoya and Jackson display phallic symbols on the sleeves of their standard-issue uniforms. Dispersed to Cole Middle School because of their ethnicity, the demographics of Cole's student body are 52% Hispanic, 44% African American, and 4% Caucasian. The school and its location is ground zero for gang activity as well as the infamous drive-by.

During their drive to Cole, Montoya is thinking of an ice breaker. Something to ease into the discussion. Cole is the first school on their list in this anti-gang agenda and the pair of officers have yet to rehearse anything, but they're both knowledgeable about gang life and can speak at great lengths about the subject.

"Maybe we can start by asking if any of 'em have seen *West Side Story*," Montoya muses.

"Jesus, Montoya! These kids are youngins, man, they ain't gonna know that shit." refutes Jackson.

"It has a good message."

"So does *Boulevard Nights*."

"Hey, now that's a good flick! . . . What you know about *Boulevard Nights?*"

"What'cha tryin' to say Montoya?"

"Nothing, brother, calm down. Okay, what about *Colors* then?"

"Now you talkin'. I'm sayin', think about all the shit we see day in and day out. We can't water it down for these kids, most of 'em are probably affiliated anyway."

"I hear ya, brother. You seen *Boyz N The Hood* yet?"

"I did. You?"

"Not yet. I want to, though. How was it?"

"It's the same shit we see here, man, no different. But they always tryin' to paint the police as the enemy."

"Motherfuckers. They should be applauding us."

"Yeah, well, if these kids don't stop killing each other it won't matter either way."

"Fuck, Jackson, when I was their age I was too busy chasin' tail to even think about being in a gang."

"Motherfucker please."

"What?"

"What happened then?"

"What you mean?"

"Your wife got you whooped."

"No she don't."

"Alright, don't call your wife then."

"I won't."

"Yeah right, she'll bust your ass if you ain't call."

"Whatever."

The Cole students already know the highlights of this lecture before it is spoken. They know the correlation between the C being X-ed out of the CR hat, and what the B being X-ed out of the Broncos hat represents, and the officers begin to think this anti-gang thing might be easier than it sounds. Next, they cover the corresponding colors and tags of the dominant gangs in the area. You have the Untouchables, (UTA) Tha Throwz, (2T) East Side Mafia, (ESM) and the Locotazo. (LCT) Tha Throwz, known as 2T for short, currently have the area locked down. They've been known to wreak havoc upon the city, and although they are from the East Side, they represent hard outside their areas, infiltrating many enemy turfs, while the increase in violence is a result of the other gangs challenging their dominance. The officers segue to the tragedy of innocent victims, and a gangsta who at 15, is sentenced to life in jail.

Montoya stands with his thumbs tucked inside his pants while tapping the front of his belt to a rhythm only he can hear. As Jackson opens the discussion to questions, Isaias immediately raises his hand and asks, "Can I hold your gun?" The officers look at each other in disbelief, they just finished their spiel about the horrors of gang life and violence in general, and how once you're in, you become property of the gang, now here comes this kid with an allure for the gun. But Isaias is persistent.

"What kind of gun is it?"

"Son—"

"YOU'RE NOT MY DAD SO DON'T CALL ME SON. My dad's locked up. My name is Isaias."

"My apologies, s—Isaias, I didn't mean anything by it, but as police officers sworn to uphold the law, we use the gun as a last resort. It's not something to play with."

"Shoot, I already held a .22 and a .38, my brother showed me, and I can shoot 'em too. Bet."

Isaias' brown eyes have both menace and realism in them, and though the officers are familiar with stand offs, they didn't expect to be tested in a classroom. Isaias knows with the teacher watching, and with the rest of the class observing every reaction of the police, that they can't do much to stifle his attitude.

The weapons hoisted on the officers' hips are on display. The others in the class didn't laugh at Isaias' requests, they too, were curious about the gun and if the officers would let them hold the steel. Enthralled by the gun, it reveals weaponized mindstates anticipating what power might feel like. What could they make people do with this power? This weapon? The plan is backfiring before ever beginning. Maybe this anti-gang work is just a dream, a pie in the sky idea that only works on paper. A few more years, and if this classroom were the streets, the officers will have to shoot their way out. In this anti-gang initiative, it'll be better to go younger, like Kindergarten, for holding the steel is better than being poor and living despicable home lives.

This glimpse of the powerless seeking power is lost on Geranimo Maestas. As the melee unravels, he's busy practicing his through the legs and around the back moves with an airless basketball. Long brown fingers performing the poetry of make-believe touch passes. This impromptu visit is such a bore, though it proved beneficial in that the pop quiz for math is postponed.

The officers planned a 45-minute speech but are only 25-minutes in when things go wayward. Montoya decides to wrap it up.

"Alright, guys, what did we learn today? . . ."

Nobody raises their hand nor blurts anything out. Both officers are eager to leave because upon entry into the class, they immediately recognized full-fledged gangstas. Some they recognize from the streets while others they spot through dress but one in particular—sporting 2T colors—has been testing them since they walked in. As the officers tried reasoning with Isaias, D-Money had pulled his black bandana from his back pocket. Now through this brief but silent tension, he wraps it around his fist on top of the desk in plain view of the officers. Bandanas like this one are forbidden on school grounds and a violation of dress code but Ms. Goff turns a blind eye, passing the buck to the officers. D-Money's hand is wrapped like a boxer, and he stares straight into Montoya's eyes—a staredown. Both officers heed this test but know where they are, including the premise of why they're inside the school. To drag a gangsta out of Cole on their first anti-gang visit is not a good look, as much as they might want to. Now Jackson attempts to close.

"Remember y'all, if you're out late be with somebody. Groups of two and even three are better than going alone. Rollin' by yourself is asking for trouble. And don't forget curfew. 9 o'clock, no one is tough enough to walk by themselves, and everyone can avoid a fight."

"Not if you're named after a Native American hero," states D-Money.

Mo looks up, immediately hearing his name invoked, and sees D-Money, who tries to maddogg but Mo just looks away.

"Yeah, I said it, go play with your little kiddies at St. Charlie's, Sitting Bull."

"I will. And it's GERANIMO," looking D-Money square in the eyes this time.

"What you say, mark?! You can't fuck wit 2T, homie!"

"Whoa, whoa, whoa, what's the fuss back there?!" inquires Jackson.

"Hey, we're not DPS, we WILL haul you down to Gilliam!" threatens Montoya.

"You wanna take a ride, son?" threatens Jackson.

"No, officer," states D-Money. D-Money has antagonized Mo ever since the elders kicked them out of St. Charles for fighting. Mo just happened to be standing at the entrance when he was thrown out.

"Guys, walking home by yourself is too dangerous. Even if it's two people, it's better than one, but more than two people is preferable," Montoya cautions.

"Wouldn't that be considered a gang?" snaps Isaias, and the

class erupts in laughter. The officers exit in a defeated manor, but the war rages on in the parking lot.

"If that little shit thinks he's gonna try to stare me down out here in the streets, he's got another thing comin' . . ."

"I hear ya, brotha, and did you see his bandana? That kid is 2T for sure . . . We'll see him again, Montoya. Believe you in me, we'll see 'em again."

THE DISS HEARD AROUND THE WORLD

MO, ZEKE, AND AMBROSE PICK me up by bike. I'm sitting on my front porch looking up at the trio watching sweat beads trickle down Mo's face. The guys pant hard and ask to kick on the hose to quench their thirst. My bike idles in the sun as the guys share drinks. It's gonna be a long trek to the East Side with the fellas. After confirming with Mo on the phone I went to Circle K to fill up my tires. We plan to hang at Mo's uncle's house who has a system that—as Mo put it—"shakes the whole damn house." When we arrive, Mo throws on DJ Quik's seminal debut, "Quik Is The Name," which is still dominating the charts. We appreciate that Quik is both an emcee and producer, and his production skills are second to none. Quik's video for "Tonite" runs nonstop on The Box.

Mo's uncle is nowhere to be found. Instead, it's a living room full of adolescent boys vying for their turn at Tecmo Bowl. I wasn't surprised Mo's uncle would entrust him enough to house sit. Gabo probably knows Mo will test the speakers and fire up the Nintendo with the neighborhood crew but why worry? Mo has the respect of his peers. Gabo also understands Mo's love for Hip Hop, reasoning that this love must quantify access to a four-tier sound system. Green and red lights dance rapidly to varying decibel levels. We need outlets like this, and Mo is eager to make it happen. I sit back, not caring about my turn for Tecmo Bowl, taking in the sounds but also feeling the vibrations of the bass and drums in my chest. Friendly competition with no beefs and Hip Hop, it doesn't get any better than this.

Mo rides with DJ Quik. Always has. And as Quik unleashes his second album upon our world we have no idea of the impact its first single will have on Denver. As soon as Quik drops "Jus Lyke Compton," he owns 1992. The video features Quik and homies boarding a bus and touring the country only to find that most major cities in America are housing gang problems just like Compton. In the track and video Quik visits Oakland, St. Louis, San Antonio, and Denver. Denver is saved for last and for good reason: he disses our town for being Compton wannabes. Denver becomes the laughingstock of Hip Hop.

Never in a million years would we have ever believed that a rapper would put our hometown in a song. We imagined it would bring credibility to the town if someone did. But then it hit. Denver is put on blast, but you know what? We bump it anyway. We love it for its brutal honesty. Truth is, we're not close to Compton in any way, shape, or form. And that's just okay. But others in the streets, most notably those from the opposing side of DJ Quik's affiliation, don't take the song lightly. To them, it's a challenge.

We're already dodging minefields in middle school hallways and the streets, gang activity rampant. But now, these gangstas we share the neighborhood with have an extra chip on their shoulders. They can't be thought of as soft and won't stand for being bottom of the barrel, especially when Quik ranked them lower than San Antonio. So, like a werewolf howling at the moon, Denver gangstas howl at a cassette tape, at a video, at someone's perception of Denver who ain't even from Denver in the first place. But if it's spoken on a record, it becomes truth.

And Denver gangstas turn more reckless. Shooting aimless bullets into the night, numbering the days until DJ Quik returns to the city but the damage is already done.

If Quik cites other cities for emulating Compton, why are they not wannabes too? Why knock only Denver? The answer lay in the verse in which Denver is dissed. Denver fools ruined a performance of his for nothing but gangsta shit. What did they think Quik was gonna do? Yet the genius of "Jus Lyke Compton" is that by hyping other cities, Quik hopes to create lifetime fans with acknowledgement and flattery. Mo, with his ear to the streets, and a heart for the best Hip Hop continues to champion Quik, diss or no diss. With Mo, it's only about the music.

In '92, rap talent can only come from the coasts, but gangs in Denver are ready to disrupt the hierarchy of coastal cities. Mo bumps "Jus Lyke Compton" on his uncle's system because it is good music. Radio stations play the edited version of the record but keep the Denver diss. Morning radio personalities make fun of the entire city for being dissed so publicly. Nobody likes to be called soft. Especially to their face. So, with one perception, one record, and one diss, the Denver streets adopt a paranoid schizophrenic mentality. Gangstas from D-Town ain't gonna play second fiddle to no one, and they salivate at the chance to prove it.

VARSITY LETTERS

PICK-UP GAMES CAN HAPPEN anywhere and everywhere. And it has always been this way. In the Sixteenth Century, Pope Gregory XIII, retroactively tweaked the Julian calendar to account for ten missing days. Due to the Julian calendar's error to properly account for the equinoxes, the day after October 4 became October 15. Yet on the other side of an ocean, and a mere 3,000 years before this tweak, Mayans were so sure of their celestial calculations that the megalithic structures they created mimicked their movements. Paralleling this time frame, Mayans —like the Olmec Civilization before them—also cut rubber from trees. One of the uses for the rubber they extracted was the laborious act of repeated layering upon a ball which began at its core and ended at its circumference. The task of intrinsically infusing the buoyancy needed to last through thousands of games of Pok-ta-Pok was indeed one of love. Their ball wasn't mass produced, it was created quite intricately, requiring the precision of a jeweler and the patience of a farmer. The subsequent buoyancy from these rubber balls were such that after thousands of years, when unearthed, was enough to out-perform a modern-day basketball. No air pumps were needed, and it didn't require a needle for inflation. After discovering a Mayan ball during an excavation, archaeologists threw it against the ground, and it bounced 18 feet off the sand. Remarkable. Would it also be a stretch to claim that Mayans created the precursor to basketball? Maybe, but whether horizontally or vertically, with Pok-ta-Pok or basketball, a sphere travels through round hoops with either a buoyant rubber ball or a pale orange dot.

Pickup games inspire unity, and by 1993, Mo's crew is now a village. He has the homies and fam from around the way which includes Ambrose, Zeke, Marcelo, and Husvaldo. He also has the youth, ages 4 through 15, who politic with Mo through the one saving grace in their community, St. Charles Recreation Center. Mo has his girlfriend, Reyna, and her friends as well as younger siblings Ray and La in his corner. Elders in the community are also supportive, like those heroic ladies and gents running the Center and volunteering to teach inner-city youth the skills of a particular sport and the intricacies of how to play on a team. Within this community—and within all communities—people know who will represent the neighborhood. One solitary leader that will speak for them on the court. The people see Mo working consistently on polishing his skill set and sharpening his sword. Even after he clocks out as an employee of St. Charles, he parlays into the gym and starts runnin'. The people get used to seeing Mo's work ethic and so naturally, they champion his quest.

Pickup games make the city smaller. Everyone wants to play against the best and thus, someone has to make the first move, whether it be a friendly invitation or through the threat of trash talk, there's only one way to supersede the hierarchy: the pick-up game. It's the only true marker to judge one's own skill level. You might be head and shoulders above the rest of your crew but then it begs the question: How good is your crew? Let your crew members gas you up and you'll be in for a rude awakening in the crosstown pick-up game. The Park Hill neighborhood has its own individual to champion. Enter Shaun "Gee" Phillips. Shaun comes up through Skyland Recreation Center and soon becomes the prodigal son of the city. But the nature of pickup games is that talent begets talent. It's why there are stories about "Earl the Pearl" Monroe before college and pros, stories resonating from pickup games. In the case of Mo Maestas and Shaun "Gee" in '93, meteorologist Larry Green could emphatically state that they'd whirlwind through the city. Though Shaun "Gee" is a year older than Mo, their paths will converge through divine order. A one on one between these two would be a sight to see, an apogee.

All is fair in love and pickup games, and you'll have to spontaneously modify your shot to particular conditions. If the rim is too bouncy, it might be better to bank it off the backboard, not to mention slightly adjusting your shot to the wind. Further adjustments are needed regarding how uneven asphalt affects your fast break. There are no fouls in pickup games, no referees. You must find a way to push through that smothering defense. There are no athletic trainers on the sidelines of a pickup game. There have been many dislocated fingers by virtue of rebounding too close to a chain net. The streets are always watching, and onlookers may be the next up. "We got next," is a universal phrase. These onlookers actively take notes about your tendencies. Do you always attack the rim going right? Always pull up for a jumper going left? You're showing your hand to your opponent and it would behoove you to have a distinguishable repertoire. Though it may seem that the next up have an advantage, they too have a line to tow. Regardless of identifying an opponent's tendencies, you have to make sure that when you're face to face with said opponent, not to overthink it. Overthinking leads to losing a single millisecond, which is all a guard needs to blow right past you.

Pickup games are universal. You can play against someone who speaks a different language from you, but the human body has a language too. In basketball it speaks athleticism and sweat beads communicate like water. Daps are universally recognized in the court of basketball affairs. Dapping an opponent before or after your game despite the outcome is an extension of Martial Arts discipline and decree. You honor your opponent and give respect to your opponent. Basketball is the world. Detlef Schrempf is from Germany, Vlade Divac; Serbia, not to mention our hometown superstar Mutombo, who's from Congo, but once a pickup game commences, a unique language is perceptible by people on every continent. It's the same from the Ruckers to Venice Beach, and furthermore from a pick-up game in Brazil to a game in China. There is nothing more human than the human body. A hook shot is ballet, a layup gives reverence to life. A pale orange dot is just another way of saying basketball is the universe.

Mo is entrenched in a pick-up game of sorts in Manual's gym and has readied his entire life for this very moment. In an introductory scrimmage against Manual's varsity, his energy is that of a shotgun blast. Layup after layup, Mo tests every sophomore, junior, and senior on the squad.

"Good job!" Coach says, "Chavez, you gonna let this kid out work ya?!" yelling at a senior guard that Mo is killing on the boards.

In every little league basketball team Mo was on it was always this way, he let his play speak for himself.

"What'chu say your name was, son?"

"Geranimo!" Mo yells while working under a screen on defense.

"What?!"

"Call me Mo!" Mo again yells as the freshman squad runs back in the other direction on a fast break.

After the scrimmage, the Coach decides that Mo will make the varsity squad, though the final roster won't be revealed until Friday afternoon upon his office door. His plan is to play him sparingly, but Coach also recognizes that Mo can act as a catalyst and reenergize a few lackadaisical seniors. In the beginning, Mo only averages a total of 9 points, but he's well on his way.

Pick-up games draw a crowd. All eyes are on the 5A basketball team from George Washington High School which features sophomore Shaun "Gee" Phillips. My sister, Angela, is attending GW for their Magnet Program and tells me about the hype around the school and the prep rallies but really, the entire city is amped. The supreme level of competition throughout Denver prep basketball raises awareness from 16th Street to Martin Luther King Boulevard, and from Federal Boulevard to Colorado Boulevard. There are bits from local sportscaster Les Shapiro on Channel 4 during the 10:30pm spots because all the high school games are commenced by then. We rely upon the *Rocky Mountain News* for box scores, and from those same box scores I also keep tabs on a certain Maestas from Manual. "Gee" has every headline, but when the George Washington Patriots play against the Manual Thunderbolts at Manual, the game is so exciting the *Rocky Mountain News* writes a feature on it. History is being made in our own backyard and its good news. It isn't about the killing spree, gang murders from Denver that are making national headlines, just talk of McDonald's All-Americans and college declarations. Mo shows up and shows out in the little time coach put him in the game, displaying streaks of genius that his coach plans to harness in the coming years. Due to the hype of the game, the seniors on the Bolts' squad would get the most action versus Shaun "Gee" and the Patriots, for this game was the biggest crowd in the Manual gymnasium since the '60s. The Patriots barely squeak out a win, but "Gee" recognizes lightning in a bottle. After the line of handshakes, he has an inquiry.

"Hey No. 9, where you play at big baller?"

"I'm down at St. Charles, come check me out, troop."

"Yo, I'll definitely check you, good game."

"Good game, we'll get'cha next time."

"Next time, huh? Alright, bet," ending on a dap.

The parking lot is a traffic jam and GW's bus is temporarily sandwiched. Honking car horns and some of that gangsta talk begin seeping through windows. "Roll 'em up!" Coach yells, but Shaun "Gee" just puts on the earphones to his Walkman as an electronic voice greets him: "Hello, this is your Midnight Marauders program . . ."

It's a golden age of Denver basketball. One afternoon, Denver Nugget LaPhonso Ellis makes an award tour around the city's high schools to display an array of dunks for the youth. Word of mouth spreads quickly. The closer one gets to the gym the louder the dunks reverberate, followed by oohs and awes. This makes his visit even more special, the fact that every hoop hopeful witnessed what type of force is needed to throw down a monster dunk at the NBA level. As weeks pass appreciation for the impromptu performance increase. Most inner-city kids in Denver never had the luxury of sitting inside McNichols Arena, so Ellis brought McNichols Arena to them. To hear the rim rocking at point blank range was something.

Competition creates mutual respect. "Gee" and his crew spill through the double doors at St. Charles Recreation Center about a half-hour before closing. They find Mo reorganizing the rec room by reconstituting the chess board with its pieces, replacing pool sticks to their upright positions on the wall, and centering the black and white players of the foosball table. Mo thrusts his brown fingers behind the back row of a rack of pool balls, slowly elevating the rack to reveal perfectly positioned orbs in a triangular shape upon faded green felt. A timid voice cuts through the breezeway.

"Hey, big baller."

"Smooth," says Mo while cracking a smile, immediately recognizing Shaun "Gee."

"We came to see how it's done."

"You talkin' pool or basketball?"

"Oh, I think you know which one."

[Slappin' fists with each other.]

"Dig this, I only got about fifteen minutes left on my shift, then we can parlay to the park cause the center's bout to close."

"You're not tryin' to delay now—"

"Actually, we can close right now," interjects Joe, the Center's Director, upon recognizing both Shaun "Gee" and the challenge that was laid before Mo. (While the challenge is Gee versus Mo, Joe sees it as another challenge: Skyland Recreation Center versus St. Charles Recreation Center.)

"Alright bet," says Shaun "Gee," rubbing his hands together.

Joe locks the doors and everyone parlays into the gym, but Mo shows concern for his duty.

"Joe, you sure it's okay that we play right now? I still haven't swept up."

"It's alright, son," Joe affirms as he wraps his arm around Mo. "You can take him!"

The remaining employees of St. Charles Recreation Center and Shaun "Gee's" crew fan out behind the three-point line and underneath the rim.

"Check ball," states Mo, abruptly sending the ball to "Gee" in one bounce.

"Don't hold back," says "Gee" as he sends the ball back to Mo backwards and through the legs.

"Gee" crouches in a defensive position while Mo stands with the basketball curled around the backside of his right forearm. Deciding if he should go left or right, drive the lane or shoot the jumper, infinite possibilities are abound.

THE STARTER JACKET

FOR ALL OF MO'S DETERRENCE of conflicts, he is constant prey to the hopeless and heartless. Individuals whose only contentment in life is to cause chaos and strife resent Mo. They are jealous of gifts bestowed upon him from the ethereal world, gifts they can feel but not touch. They hate him for his name and for the lineage that that name is linked, for the respect it commands. Mo has a way with the ladies and odds are that if a bully or gangsta or mark have eyes for a girl, that girl's eyes in turn are on Mo. His congeniality is inescapable proving both gift and curse. Factor in that Mo is not one to be punked, that he stands his ground in all situations, and therein lie a recipe for disaster.

WE ALL EMULATE OUR HEROES. Imitation is the highest form of flattery and thus—since the inception of the Fab Five—we don't own a single pair of white socks, only black. Although Nike and Jordan set trends, competitors are on a mission to catch and surpass their ubiquitous union. Derrick Coleman of the New Jersey Nets links with British Knights and Reebok goes niche with the Reebok Pump. Yet ballers prefer Jordans, and athletic types swear by the cross trainers Bo is peddling but everyone, and I do mean everyone, has to have 'em a Starter Jacket. Sure,

N.W.A. proliferates Raider gear and basically trademarks silver and black, yet Starter is instrumental in taking the fashion of emcees and making it accessible. Its accessibility doesn't make it affordable however, meaning we (our parents rather) must sacrifice hard-earned money to get it. And with any new explosion of culture or fashion—especially Hip Hop fashion—companies follow close behind, desperately trying to cash-in on our wears. [Enter Starter.]

Mo wants to buy a dapper-ass Broncos jacket and he'll sport it well—whether he buys it from Sportsfan or KMart makes no difference—but if it doesn't have that S with the Star logo above the cuff, it's not as dope. This is brand consciousness at its finest, and we, the kids buying the product, usher it in. We pay attention to it, covet it, use it to serve our vanity yet become unsuspecting targets in the process. The jacket is a bullseye, and a generation of innocence stands in between. Steve's got the all-black Bulls Starter and draws unwanted attention wherever he goes. Lonzo is bumrushed for his Giants Starter (all black with the Phil Simms GIANTS logo in black letters outlined in blue) but when his older, affiliated sister convinces a gangsta to return it, Lonzo puts it right back on again. These are the consequences we're willing to live with, to brave a hallway full of gangs to look fly. The gangs in Denver are not thought of as the most notorious in the country, but when backed into a corner, no one wants to find out how desperate they can be just to earn a rep. To propagate themselves they need the look. Unfortunately, their look and our growing fashion are one in the same, leaving us all in a grey area, dangerous ground we don't realize we're in until we face the barrel of a gun.

Despite changing color tones, gang violence gives a new meaning to the term "Colorful Colorado." Starter breaks new ground keeping black as the main color in their winter jackets. And if you've ever spent a winter in Denver, or an autumn for that matter, you'd better have a winter jacket. It can beam sunshine but blizzard the same day. You're diggin' out a driveway? Starter jacket. Waitin' for the RTD? Starter jacket. Walkin' to school? . . . A Starter is our shroud in freezing temperatures, our unzipped fashion statement in autumn breeze. We sport 'em in lukewarm temperatures as well. Too hot? Just wrap the sleeves around your waist, or worse, place the hood on your dome and let the Starter dangle from your head. As long as there's a logo attached to your body, you're in good company.

THE EMBLAZONED LOGO LETTERS raised above pitch-black cloth sear our corneas. It is art and culture, pure Americana. It isn't right, it isn't wrong: It is what it is. Children work for pennies on the other side of the globe to sew it, embroider it, just so we in the States can hurt each other for it. Sick with envy because we want it bad—paralyzed and can't move. All we can do is chase it, possess it, own it, doesn't matter who's in our way. One day we might strip it down, Flip might use nail clippers and tweezers to undo logos and patches from an all-black Jansport backpack and make it fresh. It will be a natural reaction, our counterpoint. But for now, we don't know any better. Our young minds are fertile soil and we're on the path toward consumption. To not have a brand connected to your identity is weak and powerless. Hell, The Beatles are introduced to our generation by Nike. We know nothing of revolution, only idols. But you can't denounce the world until you've lived luxuriously. And a Starter jacket is just that—luxurious.

What did Cathy tell her first-born son when he asked for a Starter?

"Mijo, you're gonna have to work for it, baby. Why don't you get a job at St. Charles? You're there all the time anyways. I can't swing something like that for you right now."

This was months ago. Now Mo has the cash saved up. He rides the bus to SportsFan. Mo loves Jordan. Every poster in his room is a Michael Jordan poster. And that is allowed, fair game. Yet there is one violation that is treacherous, even treasonous.

And that is rooting for any other football team but the Broncos. (Orange and Blue stay true!) For the last ten years some Joe Shmoe has been getting paid peddling a generic—if not clever—bumper sticker: "If God Is Not a Broncos Fan, Why Are Sunsets Orange?" Can't say that Mo ever saw an orange sunset. Lavender sometimes, pink for sure, but not orange. And there never needed to be, that's just the fanaticism he grew up with. Yet as other youth in the town jump ship and switch to teams with cooler logos or catching the national spotlight, it is important to Mo to roll with his hometown. He sees a Starter Jacket on the coat rack at SportsFan and tries it on. It fits like a glove. All white with orange creamsicle and baby blue. Butter.

Mo works hard for this freshness but many a Xmas list leave long faces because whole factions of kids don't get their Starters. John follows Mo's example, working at KFC and strolls in after Xmas break with a brand-new Nuggets joint. Some parents be caving in though. My parents have four kids, yet I begged and pleaded for the $120 pair of black and neon pink Nike cross-trainers. Their colors have a dual purpose, I like their flash plus know I won't be harassed by any gangstas, unless you count being teased for their "soft" colors as harassment. And don't tell a gangsta that real men wear pink, it will surely result in a beat-down. I'm an easy target on the streets, but Mo is on the opposite end of the spectrum, and basically requires a Starter jacket to accompany his cavalier cool. Mo's finesse is a Get Out of Jail free pass that he can wield in any situation. Remember that word again, charisma? Mo's coolness allows him to navigate a neighborhood of gangstas, fakers, big brothers, and bullies. Anointed, but it's not like he doesn't have run-ins with ruffnecks. Still, regardless of the dangers, Mo always stands his ground.

There are tormented souls out here, scorned adolescents who have never been loved, never been paid any attention, down on their luck and sick of life, prime recruitment fodder for any neighborhood gang. They feed on your suffering because they themselves suffer. It's the crabs in a bucket mentality and a theme older than the bible. The ancient saga of Good versus Evil is playing out on the streets of Denver. As Mo is beginning his path toward a bright future, a thousand demons begin clawing at his armor, pulling him into an abyss, yanking and tugging at his Denver Broncos Starter Jacket.

JEALOUS ONE'S ENVY

MO HANGS OFF THE SIDE of his mom's mattress with his back against the wall as Cathy sits on the other side, explaining, delicately, about the secret she kept for sixteen years.

"I knew it!" Mo says, leaping off the bed and standing confidently. "I knew he treated me different. That's alright, he ain't nothing but a punk now."

Less than a month after Mo's sixteenth birthday he found out that Ray Sr. was not his father. Boys are like that: trusting. They don't ask the who, what, where, or how. Tell a boy who his father is and they'll believe you, wholeheartedly. Tell 'em to run through a wall and they might break their neck doing so. Cathy had no intentions of telling Mo, but the callous nature of peers is such, that there's no place for solace or chill with banter; everything's fair game. Case in point, Mo's belief that Ray Sr. was his real dad. Cathy didn't know who told him and it didn't really matter, it was time.

Mo is affirmative. No cryin' to his Mom about the secret she kept. No worrying about the shade thrown upon him at the irresponsible Ray. No immediate wonder about his real dad. (He was never there, he ain't here now, so why worry?) Mo doesn't have a sweet sixteen. He has reality. So off into the Denver night he rolls. The cold awakens Mo. He breathes in that frigid air and consciousness fills his lungs. No shield separates him between starlight, looking up he sees marvels. Despite this harrowing news from his Mom things are actually going pretty good. Her name is Reyna Santos. She's in the same grade as Mo and lives only four blocks away.

Mo and Reyna are an item. "Don't bring no babies 'round here," Cathy warns as Mo slides into the cold. Cathy is proud though, she knew this day would come, where experimentation with the opposite would be right, would be life. She raised Mo to be chivalrous, yet also knows that handsome looks plus chivalry can cause problems he doesn't need but trusts him just the same. To Mo and Reyna this thing is sweet, like a summer bite into cold cantaloupe.

Teenage love is happiness. It's revolutionary feeling connectivity for the first time. Transferences in energy, particularly the naval and lower back that one never knew or felt, become activated. For these two it happens naturally, intended by nature—naughty by nature. For what baby boomer parents call "the birds and the bees," Mo and Reyna taste honeycomb. Teenage years are known to be the hardest, but love makes you rise. No "in love" talk yet but still, this something, this teenage love, is newness. It doesn't matter how much snow is on the ground, or how cold it is, love and newness keep 'em warm.

Mo's first stop is to his cousin, Estevan's house, who lives just down the road and will accompany Mo to Reyna's house. "If we're kickin' we're kickin', don't matter the venue," Mo says to Estevan, making sure he is comfortable with the trek. If anything, Mo does take the advice of the officers from Cole and does not walk the streets alone, but teenage love is so epic, that Mo had repeatedly journeyed solo shot to Reyna's house amidst a neighborhood of danger. Reyna always worried about him braving his way to her house, but Mo just played it down.

Mo knocks on the front door. When Reyna opens, they lock eyes and smile at each other, but her voice rises in concern, "My God, Mo, you can't just come here by yourself, it's dangerous!"

"But it's me and you now."

"Stop playin'."

"Sike. Estevan came with me."

"Where is he?"

"Yo, E!"

Estevan moves from behind the bushes and walks to the front door.

"Hi Reyna. Is your sister here?"

"No. She'll be here later though. She'll probably kick you guys out."

"Well if she kicks us out you're coming with us." Mo states with a smirk on his face as he leans in to embrace her.

* * *

A gang is an army. Members have specific duties attributed to their rank. Generals are shot-callers, boot camp is puttin' in work, and anything goes in warfare. Across the East Side a gangsta fills in for an OG who has just been locked up. D-Money was chosen due to his willingness to kick up dust and has a reputation of a stone-cold killer. Though he talks to three gangstas his same age, D-Money has earned the stripes to do so. 2T is thriving, partly due to their relentless recruitment and reckless attitude. They force all their members to earn their stripes quick-fast and in a hurry. But where Exaltted, the OG, is more calculating, D-Money is more diabolical. Exaltted arranged this meeting before he was arrested on a drug charge but trusts D-Money to relay the message of puttin' in work.

"This is our turf, represent it to the fullest. Enemies get smoked and I wanna see the three of you kick up some dust. Evade the police. If you're on foot and they roll by blend in with the landscape, make it so they don't see you, jump in tha mutha-fuckin' dumpster if you have to. BG's get caught. OG's evade. You guys need to show me something! Bring me somethin'! Show your loyalty to 2 muthafuckin' T! You marks are initiated but none of you BG's put in no work. You say you bout it, prove it. I don't care if it's a hunndo or kicks you took off some bitch, BRING ME SOMETHIN'. 2T's been around for thirty years my G's. We survive because we do the dirt. This ain't no democracy, you get a assignment, you'd betta follow fuckin' orders. You guys have a mission. I don't care who's out there tonight, show 'em 2T reigns supreme. Even if you see a grandma, take her purse and we'll buy 40's for the crew. If you see rivals, roll on them fools and represent 2T, my G's."

* * *

It didn't matter what they did as long as they were together. Hopping the RTD to the Tivoli to hold hands and kiss through a movie, sharing fries and a milkshake inside Burger King, and while in school, Mo walked Reyna to class, fingers intertwined in teenage love.

Men make advances that are ritualistic, containing a certain level of expectation, but teenage love is innocent, energetic. Moves are conducted on feel, like stepping out on faith, and eyes talk to each other in reverence. Mo stoked his fingers through Reyna's hair, and Reyna felt safe in Mo's arms.

The radio is playing SWV's "Right Here/Human Nature Mix," and it's apparent that four walls won't hold Mo—or Estevan—tonight. The song had a monster run during the summer and happens to be one of Reyna's favorite songs. The ballad fits the mood perfectly. As they stand in front of Reyna's Mom's sound system, Mo spoons her and whispers softly into her ear. But as predicted, Reyna's older sister, Lupe, comes home from work.

"What the hell is goin' on, Reyna! You fools gotta go!" Sending Mo and Estevan on their way.

* * *

Kid Rax, Vinttage and Turn-a-cutt are rollin' three deep on their mission. The city is dead tonight because it's too cold. You can own the streets on nights like this because winter puts the city on lockdown. But it makes their mission more difficult, so they stop at a corner store.

"Hey, we should rob this fuckin' shit."

"Fuck that shit my G, I'm hungry as fuck."

"Alright then, but I'm grabbing my shit and walking the fuck out. I dare that cashier to say some shit."

"You goddamn right my G, if that mark says some shit we'll take the fuckin' bread . . . And the nachos."

"Hahaha, oh shit! He said he's taking the nachos and the bread! You funny as fuck my G!!".

"I ain't playin', that cashier says one word to me and I'm dumpin'. He gonna know I stay strapped."

They post up in the parking lot of the convenience store and grub. One sees something mid-bite. "Hey, my G's, check it, over there!" The others look and see the silhouettes of two bodies walking across the street before turning out of view.

"Oh shit, I don't think these marks know what turf they in—"

"COME ON MAN, START THE CAR, LET'S GET THESE FOOLS!" says, Kid Rax, bumping the back of the driver's seat where he is sitting.

The car engine starts. They squeal the tires exiting the parking lot, throwing half-eaten nachos out the window which splatter on the ground.

"I can't wait to show these marks what's up!"

"That mark had a dope coat on, my G, that shit is mine, my G."

"Nah, fuck that, my G! I saw these marks first, that coat is mine!"

"Will you muthafuckers shut the fuck up! I think I lost 'em."

"You fuckin' dumbass."

"Fuck you, fuckin' mark."

They turn left onto East 33rd street.

"There they go right there, my G!"

"GOT their fuckin' asses!"

* * *

"She's amazing," Estevan ponders out loud, not caring that Mo can hear.

"Lupe? Man, you're trippin'," retorts Mo.

"I can dream, can't I?"

"Boyyyy ... "

"You sound like your Mom."

"Well, why don't you try rappin' to her then?"

"I'm gonna do it, primo. Bet."

"I'll believe it when I see it, E," Mo states plainly, but then reverts back to his own abilities. "I'm gonna beat "Gee" next time, E," Mo says. "He's got a hell of a shot. I was worried about him driving the lane, next time I'll focus on stopping his jumpers."

"Yeah, I heard he didn't miss at all, but you'll get him next time, primo," ensures Estevan. "When you think you'll play him again?"

"I don't know, maybe in the tournament, but that's our teams playin', as far as one on one, I don't know."

A car rolls up slow with the lights off and engine at a low hum. No screeching of the wheels. Mo and Estevan are twenty feet from the gate to Mo's house when they hear the car from behind shift into park and doors flinging open. Three gangstas spill out of the car and as Mo and Estevan turn around, they're already on them. Outnumbered, but they're in front of Mo's house so they don't run.

"What's up, thug?!" threatens Vinttage.

"What set you claimin', fool?" Turn-a-cutt inquires, but it's not rhetorical.

"We don't claim nothin', this is my house," Mo says confidently.

"Fuck your house. What you got on my jacket, homie?!" states Vinttage, grabbing Mo's jacket by the shoulder but Mo shrugs him off.

Turn-a-cutt pulls out a gun and points it at Mo.

"We're takin' the jacket, mark!" yells Cutt.

"No you're not!" Shouts Mo and leaps hands first grabbing the gun.

Mo wrestles the gun from Cutt on some Jackie Chan before Jackie Chan was the man type shit. But Kid Rax pulls out a— POP! POP! Mo is floored. Estevan hit, and staggering.

2T scatters as fast as they came. Mo is down. Estevan sways to the front door, mortified. He doesn't know their condition. They need an ambulance or they'll die. Mo tries standing but collapses into snowpack. "GO, GO, GO, G!" yells Kid Rax and tires screech into the night. Mo starts crawling to the house. Ray and Cathy are already running through the house to the front door to see about the gunshots. Cathy opens the door to Estevan, who's bloodied up.

"DON'T LET ME DIE, AUNTIE!"

"WHERE'S MO?!!"

Although tragedy strikes here on earth, angels are rejoicing. Mo is going home. Transcending. You rise to see yourself, the physical proof of your transcendence, in your body. Before this jump, you held on, to the grunt, the effort, what was natural as breathing you have to work for now. You rise and find that in this dimension there is no effort—there just is. There are no gunshots. Time doesn't exist in this dimension. You see all thirty years of the movement at once, you see your birth, you see ancestors and your jacket disappears and reappears as you blink. You see yourself dropping 50 on Machebeuf, see "Maestas" on the back of your jersey. Reading psalms to Ray. Hugging La. You see light. Ferromagnetism.

The spectrum is revealed to you. You don't feel the cold. Your body collapses and slams into snowpack on the side of the house. Consciousness never was this much of a fight. A veil is lifted. Get mom, get Ray, get to La. Get somewhere. I can do this. I can't feel my legs. Dizziness. There's so much blood it seeps and seeps and seeps. Red in white snow. White snow is red liturgy. "I know their faces." His face was scared. I'm gonna make it. They won't win. We'll get em and triumph. Crawling back to the essence. "This is for my ... See you when I get there." Lord, let me just look at my family one time, that's all."

"MA, I FOUND HIM, HE'S BACK HERE!!" Ray calls from the back of the house.

Cathy runs to the back and finds Mo in a pool of blood. Mo can't speak and his eyes glance upon his mother one last time. He slips in and out of consciousness. His moans have a gurgle.

"CALL 911!" she shouts to Ray but sirens already wail in the distance.

Shot for an orange, white, and blue-something gangstas scatter leaving Mo trudging through blood-clotted snow. The ambulance comes but it's too late. A pronouncement will soon follow. Time stops and sound ceases but for an echo of the gun blast folding into eternity. Yellow tape secures the perimeter. Red handprints and a trail of blood spewed by the struggle of a teenager's corpse is all that remains. Mo's potential vaporized. A life in sixteen movements.

Hey Sixteen, your energy never bickered. It flowed with no damns, no shits, and no toothpicks. Hey Mo, miraculously, your vibration stayed pure through this maliciousness known as the world. Hey Sixteen, we witness your purity, your light, and we'll witness your transcendence. Hey Mo, you were unmovable and immeasurable, living every day as a treasure. Hey Sixteen, we're glad we followed you to wherever you wanted to go. Hey Mo, you touched our souls the way no one ever has.

Mo's eyes are closed.

MIQUIZTLI

"WE COULDN'T SAVE THEM BOTH," Officer McCurley says forth-right, hoping to evade a rebuttal. "It was out of my hands," McCurley adds as Cathy's universe crumbles. The tears pouring from her eyes make him angry inside. Not in the sense that he wished he could've done more, but as he reckoned, 16-year-old Geranimo Maestas was "in the streets," essentially "dancin' with the devil." If Mo was indeed unaffiliated—as Cathy proclaims— then what to make of this awful tragedy? To Officer McCurley, rare is a crime scene that doesn't contain the fingerprints of two rival gangs. It's the first 48 and Officers McCurley and Stanton tell Cathy she better fully comply with the police department if there is to be any hope of apprehending Mo's killer. Yet for Cathy, the gestures, hindering and looking down upon by Officer McCurley cannot be ignored.

McCurley glances at Cathy's two younger kids in the back-ground. They sit side by side, hands clasped together with tears in their eyes. The scene makes him uncomfortable for a moment until Stanton nudges him to snap out of it. Officer McCurley presses again, "So you're saying that your son was not affiliated with any gangs, Mrs. Maestas?"

"I ain't gonna tell a lie to you's guys in order to find my son's killer, if you can't believe he wasn't in a gang then that's on you!" Cathy yells. "He . . . " but Cathy breaks down into tears. She wants to tell them that Mo had a girlfriend, a part-time job at St. Charles Recreation Center and that he had made the varsity squad in basketball for the Manual Thunderbolts, but she can't muster the fight. Shock, heartbreak, numbness takes control of her body making it hard to breathe. On the first day of the rest of her life without her eldest son, there couldn't be any mourning, and no peace.

Mo was shot in his main artery, losing too much blood to be resuscitated. So could Officer McCurley have said it better? Absolutely. But Cathy's adept at reading between the lines, forever suspicious of what lies beneath. "We couldn't save them both," McCurley said, but his smug attitude tells a different story. Though her ears are numb, the officers also relay that Estevan is laid up in Denver General hospital in critical condition—shot twice—but alive. The officers then leave the Maestas residence still skeptical of Mo's supposed unaffiliation.

Was Officer McCurley a surgeon? Hands up by his face dipping his elbows in sanitizer. Was Cathy supposed to nod her head in agreement, justifying this decision posthumously? "We couldn't save them both." It is cold, blunt, typical jargon from a Gang Unit officer. Cathy lost her son. And Mo was a victim of gang violence. Wouldn't that quantify the means in the moment to try and save Mo also? But Officer Harry McCurley viewed all youths as juveniles. He grew up in south Texas and took the role of cowboy seriously during the Summer of Violence.

For the rest of us, we lose our binary star: Geranimo Maestas. Losing power yet still emitting light through our universes. His blood steeped in virgin white snow from the night before. His life lost to gang violence for something as trivial as a jacket.

"We couldn't save them both," Officer McCurley reasoned. Verdict and sentence. A swift mallet strike to the pulpit: "We couldn't save them both because they were out in the gang-ridden streets. How dare they live joyously amongst this hell. How dare they gallivant to the store with no feeling of fear. How dare they exist."

The Denver Police Department gives no training on how to inform a grieving mother that their child has been murdered. So, it goes without saying that uttering those five words to Cathy in the way he did, Officer McCurley would forever be perceived as insensitive, if not barbaric. Was this the first time he had to deliver such news? Was it the most difficult part of the job? Do these factors matter to a grieving mother? "We couldn't save them both," Officer McCurley spewed, biting down on a tan toothpick protruding from the left side of his mouth, evidence of a swing shift lunch, his daily routine unaffected by tragedy.

Preparations must be made for Mo's rosary and funeral. Cathy takes no tranquilizers, no valium. She must maintain a clear head through this. She can't be subdued in any way. She remains an example to Ray and La in this most tumultuous time. To feel this excruciating pain without anything artificial. Most importantly, she prays.

THE ROSARY

IT IS A FREEZING NOVEMBER NIGHT, and the lit steeple illuminates darkness. My dad drops me off on the street corner, winter jacket zipped to my chin. I don't need to hear my dad's words nor hear the word son. I need to feel this emptiness. To be absent of dialogue so I can revere the life of my friend, not to be befuddled by the living. In the days following Mo's murder I vow to keep him in my heart forever. I also know that Cathy, Ray and La will keep his candle burning until the end of time. Everything Mo had he gave to us. Not legally a man yet but I tell you he was a man, a man who stood for something. And that—in itself—stood for something. Too many of us gave up our jacket or gear or shoes willingly. We lacked backbone. Mo sensed something inherently wrong with this dynamic. He just didn't know how desperate and callous our peers could be. This is hell.

Mo's murder is the shot heard throughout Denver, amplifying what's going on in the streets. To this point it was only gang on gang violence. After Mo's murder we are all put on notice. Yet before we wish to reclaim our streets, we must honor his life. To revere what would never be again. Or so we thought. We cry. Oh boy do we cry. The idols lining the Church add to feelings of emptiness. The frigid Denver night. Our slow-paced prayers. Stained glass and candlelight mixed with mourning. We don't want to leave the presence of Mo's body. Our brightest star, Geranimo Maestas, stood up to the gangstas and paid the ultimate price. The pain emitting from Cathy's wails transport me back to 1989, to a simpler time, a time of peace and happiness.

Death too, is an epidemic. Unwittingly tragic.

* * *

Before the Rosary commences there is another congregation of sorts, though most in the church have no idea that it's happening. It is a shield, a human force field of fortified love. Mo's biological father—genetically his dad but renouncing Mo for all 16 years of his life—arriving now at the tragic end when he denied him from the very start. But the people at the wake tonight will do anything for Mo—even in death. Mo's biological was still trapped in the perception that genes made him a father. Bullshit. With Cathy's love and guidance, Mo figured it out on his own. Nothing was lacking. Mo's brethren stand firm in solidarity, blocking the entrance with crossed arms, their eyes piercing through Mo's biological's soul.

"You never claimed him," said Zeke.

"You never even tried," said Ambrose.

Mo's biological is ostracized from this gathering of love and the night brings the cold memory of relinquishment, and he hates himself for denying one of life's greatest gifts, one that he would never know. He retreats on his own accord, despondent and weak, greeted by nothing but icy asphalt.

* * *

After viewing Mo's body, the line conjugates to his family in the front row and I don't know how best to console Ray, La, and

Cathy but the line is quickly moving. Mo's many friends are in attendance and we all want to say goodbye, so I keep moving too, briefly hugging them all.

Back at my seat I look around the church. I see Pablo's muscles protruding his sweater and know that sheer force can't bring Mo back. All our prayers can't do it. And the mass of all our tears can't help either. Nor do the testimonies of Mo's friends in attendance. Neither the preacher nor the pulpit has the power to resurrect. We realize our homie isn't ever coming back and forever is a mighty long time.

* * *

What we're about to witness is paradoxically devout. It's about how a song titled "Gangsta Lean" becomes the soundtrack to Mo's rosary. Gangs make it so dismal that even your neutrality gets tested. And Mo's confident neutrality, in addition to his unapologetic self-expression, was a threat to their domain.

DRS's "Gangsta Lean" came out last month, and with its straightforward and specified title, one would be hard pressed to imagine the ubiquity of the song or the impact of its lyrics. "Gangsta Lean" is urban. It holds a mirror to our forlorn reality and dire streets, while conjuring divine messages for grieving communities.

It's mind-boggling that "Gangsta Lean" was released before Mo's untimely death—and that he liked it—and that it peaked at No. 1 on the Billboard R&B charts in early November, and that tragically, it becomes the soundtrack for those of us trying to cope with his murder. Mo listened to it as Walkman earphones laced his ears, wire descending into the orange interior lining of his inside pocket, as his hands sprung and flung a basketball between he and the Earth. Yes, Mo jammed out to the song that would frame his eulogy.

They're playing "Gangsta Lean" ceremoniously! In the

Catholic Church no less! Some might think we're contradicting ourselves, that playing a song with a connection to gang culture at Mo's wake is sacrilege. Yes, the horrible fact remains that Mo was slain in the streets by what are probably gangstas. Mo's murder was a robbery attempt—a jack move if you will—gone wrong. This was definitely a gangsta scenario, so it might seem cold, callous, unjustified to laud a song from a gang's perspective yet herein lies the paradox: Mo was striving to make the most of his adolescence and didn't live parallel to gang culture, he lived within gang culture. In other words, gang culture was in his neighborhood meaning he—like it or not—was constantly surrounded. It was as much a part of him as basketball. And only those with supreme confidence—as was the case with Geranimo Maestas—never changed an ounce of how they're gonna live in this gang-wrought territory.

Lines become blurred, and the waters, muddier, because at the time of Mo's rosary we don't yet have confirmation if a gang is involved but for this brief moment in time, the only thing that matters is Mo's memory. We know our purpose for the song and the direction of our endearing love. We blast its vibrations to the people, to Mo, to God. "Gangsta Lean" possesses an unmatched alchemy. Our intent is to honor our brother.

Only God can judge us.

* * *

After the rosary, many things remain undone. Mo's investigation is in full swing and his funeral is soon to be scheduled. The rosary provides some closure, albeit mournful, and the faintest glint of positivity shines through. Is this God's plan? Is Mo his beacon? Are the stars aligning to something cathartic? Cathy begins to believe that she is on the precipice of something spiritual, divine even, and her intuition becomes blessed with both future and foresight.

Cathy and her kids arrive home after a long and emotional night. After putting Ray and La to bed she comes to the realization that it's only her, God, and the four walls. She clutches the Bible so tight it warms her cold fingers. She opens the book randomly but what she reads in that moment begins a new chapter in her life. From this day forward she will live anew, propelled by faith and always believing that Mo's story can teach. It coincides with scripture, and she will display it on the mantle for her, and all her descendants thereafter. It is Mathew 5:9 *Blessed are the peacemakers, for they are the children of God.*

THE FUNERAL

ON THE DAY OF MO'S FUNERAL, I was angry at life. All these fools that never hung around Mo were going. Gettin' out of school for the sake of gettin' out of school. I thought it was about me. It wasn't.

Jerry was takin' damn near everybody to the funeral, and this could be accomplished by means of his truck. I felt pinned to the ground and was considering going with Jerry—I didn't have a ride—but I also didn't want to witness my homie being lowered into the ground. In my mind I made it about everybody but me so I could keep up this charade of running from pain.

My parents didn't ask me how I was dealing with Mo's murder. Instead I lived with a cacophony of thoughts that were muted by the harrowing murder numbers being purported by the news which was much more concerned with these murders' percentages than the actual victims. Every day missin' Mo. Every day running from the pain.

COINTELMO

CATHY PULLS MO'S PHOTO FROM her back pocket and dusts it off, clutching it with her curled finger and thumb, holding it as if a totem, Mo's smile transcending time and space.

"My son Mo was murdered last week," pleads Cathy.

She stops them as they walk home from school. High school kids, middle school, even elementary. Somebody knows something. If the neighborhood is six blocks wide, and there's thirty houses per block, how will she talk to 180 families? One door at a time. Cathy is not the type to lock herself in a room and feel sorry for herself. Neither she nor her son will be intimidated by gangs. Similarly, despite the DPD giving dead ends she won't let their inaction turn Mo's murder into a cold case. At least Cathy knew from Estevan's first-hand account that their verbiage was consistent with gangstas. Plus, they wore 2T bandanas—another vital link. Yet without names or identifying tattoos or even a make or model on the car (Estevan described it as "boxy," probably an old Buick or Oldsmobile) the DPD threw up their hands. Everything happened so fast, they ran up from the back, that Mo and Estevan were more concerned about survival than identifying markers.

The time is now. Not only does the DPD brand Mo a gang member but they're overwhelmed by what's being called the "Summer of Violence." By late 1993, media outlets dub Denver as "Little LA." Cathy keeps Mo's picture handy in case she needs to wield it on someone who is on the fence between talkin' and tellin', determined to uncover information in this Eastside labyrinth of black bandanas. Cop show detectives slam their victim's photo on the interrogation table for maximum effect, but Cathy has stake in the game. She knows her victim and hopes Mo's congenial face can tip the scales in her favor.

Watch thy enemy. Not only in battle but after the fall. Street gangs in many ways mimic the government, law enforcement, and military arm. Tactics are the same. If you try to overthrow something corrupt, you become corrupt in your attempt, there is no way around it. This is part of how gangs ascend the hierarchy of neighborhoods. Cathy is one woman against what seems like the entire world. Tha Throwz are deeply rooted in the neighborhood, press coverage in the *Rocky Mountain News* paints the situation on the streets as hopeless, nobody wants to drop a dime and yet, Cathy had been in a similar situation before. She was one of many that helped in picking up the pieces of the bombing of the Downing building where the Raza would sleep. As part of the Crusade for Justice, Cathy witnessed the government's endless resources, including the propaganda levied against their cause from newspapers and news stations, and from the vitriol of their opposers.

This witnessing wasn't given to Cathy in a classroom. Before tonight, this knowledge of the FBI's relentless infiltration of the Chicano Movement and the Crusade for Justice was only a searing memory of how we were so close to unification but duped and stricken right before our pinnacle. This vision of self-reliance billowed away in gray smoke from thrashed windows. Now in '93, she alone will have to ensure that Mo's pinnacle won't evaporate in gun smoke.

The CIA operates in Tertia Optima, which means you can't kill someone you're not at war with. It would make their linkage of the Chicano Movement to the USSR, and communism in general, look like the next logical step in their playbook. Yes, when people see value in themselves it is a threat to the controlling system. This bogus claim by the FBI was both reactionary and desperate. Like casually linking Mo's murder to him being gang related. It is lazy. The DPD was blasé about having Cathy dispute that detail of the investigation. Yet Cathy knows semantics is key. She will never stand for this linkage. She knows the truth.

Looking at Cathy one can see many things. Grief, heartache, but the one thing they can't see that is prevalent in all she does, hiding underneath grief: is justice. While Mo lay facing the top of a casket, Cathy searches for justice, crusades for Justice. Never had her witnessing of infiltration come in handy before. Maybe this remembrance could help her infiltrate the streets of her neighborhood. She knows Mo's killer is hiding in plain sight. It's time to bring him out.

Cathy will make you believe you can do the right thing by divulging information. She also makes you believe you can do the impossible. Cops click pens and take statements; Cathy did the opposite. "I'm gonna take it to the streets," she said, "The people know." When she called the police station, they took a message. Her calls weren't returned and when they were: dead ends.

Investigators become frustrated by the interest she has in the case. They're also offended by her premise that they won't find Mo's killer.

"Send them Gang Unit cops to ask questions about the gangs in this neighborhood. I know you guys have the resources."

"Ma'am, we're doing the best we can—"

"Well I ain't gonna wait on you's guys, I can get out there and ask questions too!"

At their weekly check-in with the captain, Detectives Schotter and Grabel make mention of Cathy. They describe her as a "pesky" mom tying up their time.

"Well if that lady wants to take this investigation over so be it, we got too much shit going on anyway," says Captain Newcomb to his cohorts. "Just play dumb and give her the same spiel. She'll get tired of calling, eventually, Schotter."

"You got it, captain. We got these fuckin' kids dying every single day. She thinks her son is the only one. We don't have enough body bags to keep up with these dead kids."

Yet much to Schotter's chagrin, visibility is Cathy's strength. She will shine the light of justice in all the cracks and crevices of Eastside Denver. As sure as the city breathes it tells a story, but you need to put your ear to the street to hear its rhythm.

Cathy remembers this game of cat and mouse when the Crusade demanded better treatment from the police. It was a murdered teen at the hands of the DPD in the 60's that prompted the Crusade for Justice. Now Cathy will crusade for her own murdered son's memory. COINTELPRO, the FBI's counterintelligence program was responsible for our division, and many lives were at stake in the name or liberation and justice. So, in '93, as before, bringing Mo's murderer to justice carries the same heavy air. It's the final countdown between her and the damned.

Cathy has the lessons of the Chicano Movement, a guiding light for the people and a sharpened sword to the oppressors. She changes the semantics of Mo's case and becomes the face of his investigation. By changing the semantics, she changes the perception. And perception is reality. People seeing her in the community on a mission made them want to help. When a person takes a stand, people tend to follow. The fact that Cathy is willing to be seen in the streets after her son is slain is inspiring. Mo's family and friends become an army of soul survivors taking his memory up and around the city. The streets is watching. And Cathy receives the tip she's been praying for: The most unassuming witness in the most 2T-infested block of Eastside Denver.

STREETS IS WATCHIN'

TELLEY FIGEROA SEES A FLYER on a streetlamp post. Mo's picture is in the center. It has a phone number dubbed vertically on the bottom though none of the fringes are tore off yet. Telley gazes at the photo and gets a warm feeling followed by sadness. The only one who was ever nice to him was Mo. No one ever saw Telley and if they did, they made fun of what they saw. He was locked in a perpetual state of childhood due to his stature. It didn't help that he walked home solo shot from St. Charles every night. At first, he was afraid of the evening air but figured that if people punked him during daylight, then there was no difference in being punked at night. From that point on he expected bullies to come popping out of trees like a Geto Boys video, but instead of the similar sized Bushwick Bill, it was 2T.

"Damn Tellz, your head so fuckin' square I can even see yo azz at night!!" barked Turn-a-cutt.

If Mo had the courage to stand up to 2T then Telley could at least muster the courage to tear off the number. "Fuck these muthafuckas," he thought, "Mo was better than all of them put together!" Telley looks around a couple times then tears off the number. Instead of stashing the number in his wallet, he places it in the one spot he knows he won't forget it, between the Swisher box and the cellophane surrounding it. He slides the paper fringe into the cellophane and pulls out another wood tip. He lights it with a green plastic lighter he copped at 7-11. He's saving up for a metal Zippo. After the Zippo, a leather jacket. He's got the whole thing planned out.

"Maybe I'll keep the number on my dresser for a while," Telley thinks to himself.

Becoming a teenager has done nothing for Telley's size. He's only the teenage version of the short kid with the boxy head. People still ridicule him so Telley does the one thing that makes himself look older: he starts smoking. According to Telley, it doesn't matter if you're ugly or beautiful, man or woman, or tall or short, smoking cigarettes just looks fucking cool. He smokes so much he graduates from Camels to Swisher Sweets, blowing smoke through his nose like he's in deep contemplation, the thick cigar smoke dancing out his nostrils.

2T forgot about Telley. They harassed him so much it wasn't even fun anymore. Now when they see him, they merely bump him out the way. And they see him quite frequently, for Telley lives on 35th and Humbolt, the same block as Turn-a-cutt. It's a 2T hangout where the fellas smoke chronic in the backyard of Turn-a-cutt's grandmother's house, who yells at the slew of them to keep it down. They simply raise the volume on their boombox to drown out her yells. This is their house, their hood, and soon, their city.

The dominion gangs wield is strengthened when people feel they have something to lose. Everyone has fears of confrontation and death, but if those fears are properly ignited within us, gangs can do as they wish. Telley harbors horrid memories of the multiple times 2T threw him against a brick wall. Once, they strangled Telley's throat against the bricks for so long he passed out. Another instance found them tossing his backpack on the roof of an abandoned house.

Who in their right mind would want to finger 2T? It's sure to be a death sentence. And walking on the other side of the block won't do any good because they own both sides. Yet sometimes it's not only a rival gang that makes a gang falter. Sometimes it's pride. A few weeks after Mo's murder, Kid Rax, Vinttage, and Turn-a-cutt were on the way to bootleg some brew and started discussing the jackin' that went wayward. Telley was dropping salt on the sidewalk on the side of his house when he heard, "If that fool woulda gave up the goods I wouldn't have smoked him, my G." Telley couldn't differentiate between the three and moved his head to see who was talking. That's when they noticed Telley and quickly jumped the fence, backing him against the bricks of his own house.

"You didn't hear SHIT, right, Tellz??" But Turn-a-cutt's grip was so tight he couldn't speak. Kid Rax hits Cutt on the back and says, "Let's go. This fool ain't gonna say shit, he'll probably shit his pants first before he says shit . . . " And they dropped Telley on the icy concrete on the side of his house. Confident he never heard anything, and if he did, sure of themselves that he would never tell.

Yet the grace Mo showed Telley was reciprocated in his confession. Telley took Mo's murder to heart. He knows all three of them. The only thing he doesn't know is who pulled the trigger. Even Cathy is thrown off by Telley at first. She's looking at this teenager who is small in comparison to the size and shape of his squared head. Another dead end. "This kid can't divulge any secrets," she thought. "He'd be dead in a day." Yet nothing could be further from the truth. After telling Cathy what he knows Telley stands 10-feet tall.

It's Telley. Telley mutha-fuckin' Figeroa. For years he was picked on and picked apart. This is poetic justice. Cathy plans to hit the police station in the morning. Dominoes are about to fall.

CURSE OF A PREDICATE FELON

KID RAX, AKA JUVENILE 180066, was enjoying the bus ride from juve to the big time. In the real-world people do crazy things like speeding to red lights and stopping abruptly or pumping gas while rubbernecking the road. Smells of oil and pollution permeate the city. To Rax this is the sweetest smell ever. Pollution smells of the world. Of hustle and bustle. Not of cells and juve pods. Rax loved going outside at Gilliam Juvenile Detention Center for this very reason. The exhaust from cars made him temporarily forget where he was and how he got there.

Rax doesn't think about the life he took, nor the jacket that led to pulling the trigger. His singular thought is freedom. Though the United States is the land of the free and home of the brave, poverty shackles feet, and nobody wants to be poor and alone. At least with a gang, you have power in numbers. Whoo-ridin' was adrenaline, and the rush Kid Rax felt released the grip of those shackles. Thus, Rax only felt worthy when dominating people. He felt rich. It felt like currency.

That is until November 26, 1993. That night was an anomaly. Before that run-in Rax shot bullets into the night sky, old oak trees, and vacant houses. None of them were direct hits. Instead they ricocheted off poverty's rusted chains. Aimless fits of rage never had any consequences. An affiliation and a gun were all that was needed to terrorize the world. Nobody ever put up a fight, and Rax began to think that no one ever would. Gangstas die at the hands of other gangstas. In a cloud of dust and gun smoke. But 180066 had a mother hunt his ass down. Not exactly a gangsta's fairytale he wished to own.

"No one ever cared when I was poor and struggling," Rax thought to himself, "The only time anyone cared about me was when I was stickin' up muthafuckas."

Rax once kicked a toddler right out of his stroller. The toddler's mom, as offended as she was that Rax made her toddler cry, took one look at his black bandana and put her head down, grabbing her toddler and pushing the stroller in the opposite direction. Rax did all this simply because he could. One look at his colors and people took the humiliation because they feared the consequence.

The bus turns onto the highway and Rax wonders what his cell mate might be like in the big time. Upon Rax's arrival at Gilliam, he was thrown into a pod with Damien, a notoriously small and shifty Hispanic, a tagger with no affiliations and a fervent curiosity for the dark realm. So much so in fact, it made Rax uncomfortable. The spectacles Damien sported made him look like some kind of evil genius. After hours of silence, Damien finally broke the ice and asked Rax a question.

"You ever heard of Natas?"

"Huh?" Rax questioned back. "What'chu talkin' bout, thug?"

"You know, Hip Hop. You ever heard of a group called Natas?"

"Nah, thug, never."

"They rap about the dark realm."

"You mean these thug-ass streets?!! I'm 2T, flea!! We own these muthafuckin' streets!!"

"Yeah, I've seen your emblems. I'm a writer, but I got caught. I ditched my bag under the bridge, but the cops found it, six cans of Krylon with the tips for the fat-letter spray."

"So you one of those tagger muthafuckas, huh?"

"Yeah man, I be bombing the shit out of this city! Rollin' at night be like the dark realm."

"What the hell you talkin' man? You heard of Snoop Doggy Dogg, right?"

"That shit's alright. But it's not dark enough."

"So you on some commando-ass Rambo-type shit then?"

"Not like that, think about it. What is Natas spelled backwards?"

Kid Rax takes a second then his brow raises slightly. Damien smiles wickedly as if conveying to Rax that although unaffiliated, he rolls with something much more sinister.

Rax thinks to himself, *this little scrawny-ass Mexican dude is ill!*

Rax says, "Look, I ain't into that devil shit, thug."

"It's all good. You should check it out sometime though."

"I ain't gettin' out this bitch for a while so maybe, I ain't got nothing but time."

"What you in for?"

"Murder."

A thought grew in Rax's mind that night. He began to see that gang life only prepared him for war with other gangs. Despite 2T's rep, they weren't running Gilliam and his affiliation didn't mean shit to Damien. Poverty and the streets were bad but navigating incarceration—even in juve—would mean starting all over again. It was true that being from the most notorious set in Denver counted for something, but it was also true that Kid Rax would forever be surrounded by boys—and soon enough, men—with nothing to live for.

Less organization in juve meant that everyone was out for themselves. Complete chaos surrounded Rax every hour of each day. On the streets Rax had a legion, representation, but in juve, those incarcerated nuts under the age of 18 were straight wildin'.

Because most juves were heading straight for the big time after their 18th birthday, meant they tried early and often to establish a reputation.

Kid Rax was even tested the night before this infamous bus ride—his final night in juve. He wished to relax in his pod during the hour free time and take in his last night in Gilliam since Damien went into the open area. Rax didn't wish to politic with the others nor play dominoes. He barely rested his head onto the cot when somebody startin' bangin' on the door. Fuck that— somebody was beatin' the muthafuckin' door down!

"Come out you fuckin' piece of shit!! Face me like a man, bitch!! Without your gang you ain't shit!! You killed my homie!! Let's see if you can hang, bitch!!"

Kid Rax jumped off the cot but stayed in the pod. He figured this was another test. Another loose cannon looking to earn some stripes because he was 2T.

Rax looked through the rectangular window as fists hit the door creating booming thumps.

Rax didn't recognize this madman with rage in his eyes, looked into the free area behind him and saw Turn-a-cutt watching this chaos with no sense of concern.

Rax, still in shock from this impromptu challenge, in waiting for this madman to stop bangin', or for the guards to take him down, had to save face, because everyone was watching so he threw up 2T signs while yelling back.

"THIS 2T MUTHAFUCKA!!"

No sooner than Rax started yelling a guard hit the madman with a baton which dropped him on the floor. But restraints couldn't shut him up.

Rax saw him earlier at dinner, starin' like he had a vendetta.

Rax thought, "He's sayin' I murdered his friend. The kid with the jacket? He wasn't bangin'. That kid has people? Enough to wanna test 2T? . . . "

That single incident made Kid Rax believe that he would

never be safe. Prison bars couldn't protect him from the lifestyle he chose, neither could his affiliation. As the bus approached the big time, he reflected on Turn-a-cutt's reaction—or lack of one.

"When I see Cutt again," Rax thought, "It's on!"

He didn't even rep the set. Rax couldn't believe it. He has the audacity to let some mark-ass busta bang on my door like that?

Kid Rax hoped the big time would be more like the streets where power in numbers reigned supreme. Rax also hoped that 2T would be more prominent, he didn't want to worry anymore about wannabe tagger devil worshippers or loose cannons or fools who can't rep the set. He wanted to be a dominant force on a winning team. Yet slowly, Kid Rax began to become a victim of his own circumstance.

HOUSE OF PAIN

Turn-a-cutt arrives to the big time two weeks after Kid Rax. He sees Rax in the cafeteria and asks about the ropes.

"It's not Kid anymore, it's Raxx OG, and your head's fucked up if you think I forgot about your sorry ass. Give me one good reason why I should help you."

"What, fool?!! You betta watch what the fuck you sayin'!!"

"Or else what, thug?!! You think you can threaten me?!! I'm the one who saved your ass that night and blasted those fools!!"

And fists started flying. The Conglomerate—a penitentiary network of 2T and ESM—stand and watch.

Exaltted, an OG from 2T but now sole leader of The Conglomerate, speaks to his second in command, Fortittude, as prison guards are dispersed and soon disrupt the melee.

"These rookies don't know shit. Letting personal feuds cloud their loyalty, undermining the hierarchy of this here. Look around, other networks are clowning us right now. How the fuck we keep our edge when rookies like this fuck it up? This can't be tolerated. I don't care how long these muthafuckers stay down, they gotta learn."

"What you want me to do, boss?"

"Give Rax a warning, and ask him who the fuck this guy is, it looks like he know this fool."

"And the other?"

"Make sure he knows who we are."

"You got it, X."

Both Rax and Turn-a-cutt are hauled to solitary confinement; one-week stints. It's Turn-a-cutt's first day and the guards issue a beat down before they lock his darkened cell. Turn-a-cutt has no idea of the dangerous ground he now stands upon. It's day one and he never receives a briefing on the hierarchy. He thought he'd always have some type of 2T shield, and that his altercation with Rax was no different from a sibling rivalry. He couldn't have been more wrong. Entrance to The CG isn't automatic. Streets are streets but prison is prison. He'll have to earn his way in.

When Cutt is released from solitary confinement nobody will eat with him in the cafeteria. Not a good sign at the start of his sentence, but he knows enough to pinpoint the hierarchy of The Conglomerate. He focuses on a table containing the leaders. It has to be, he figures, because the table sits adjacent to the wall. Kid Rax is seated at the next table over, creating a barrier between the rest of the cafeteria and the high command: lookouts and security detail. Reeking of desperation, Cutt questions anybody and everybody as members leave the table, careful not to run into Rax. The Conglomerate didn't savor Turn-a-cutt's cavalier attitude which resulted in a squabble, thus resulting in other prison gangs questioning their solidarity, and they surely don't need a gangsta who is hard-up. CG members repel him like bug spray and entrance is denied before it's even considered. Cutt is shocked to his core, not even a chance to enter. He knows that without representation, he'll be tested repeatedly.

"Kid Rax is behind this," Turn-a-cutt tells himself, "If I can't join the CG, I'll make sure he gets his."

Cutt joined 2T when he was only 11 years old. He hadn't

known anything else but 2T through his adolescence and teenage years. "Hell, I was 2T before Rax!" Cutt thought, vengefully.

Turn-a-cutt lasts three months. He can no longer take the cell inspections, frequent tests from the inmates, harassment from the guards, and the constant stress of having to watch his back. In every waking moment he's obsessed with lightening his load. Ninety days is a lifetime without gang. A prison reject is worse than being a nobody and he reaches his most desperate point. "Anything will be better than this," Cutt ponders, but his thoughts cascade from raging vengeance to contemplating a plea. Dime-dropping and plea copping have never been attributes of anyone involved with 2T but now Cutt is solo-shot. Running with 2T is all but a distant memory for Cutt and he figures he's good as gold to drop a dime.

To get Rax back for the treason he committed will be the only silver lining to look forward to. Others had copped. And others had succeeded in evading the label and stigma of prison reject. Cutt visited the library and found out how to contact a lawyer. Maybe, just maybe he had some information that was valuable. All Cutt knows is that Vinttage must be at a different facility because he shipped out to the big time before Rax. When word comes back on Rax, Cutt will defect his snitchin' onto Vinttage to keep him guessin'. It's a fool-proof plan, and Cutt's hopes are to be released from prison due to his cooperation.

The act of turnin' on a gangsta whom Cutt had been down with for years would be hard. Cutt reasoned that if he couldn't join The CG then he would have no recourse but to bury Kid Rax. With Telley's identification of these three, they knew one of them had pulled the trigger on the fatal shot that killed Mo but weren't sure which one. These 2T gangstas stuck vehemently to the code. They are hardened gangstas but as Turn-a-cutt is about to prove, not hardened criminals. One conversation with the law is one conversation too many. Cutt's lawyer is selling him pipe dreams yet he was so drunk on revenge he couldn't see it. The only two things Cutt can visualize is revenge and lightening his load.

There was but one roadblock standing in Turn-a-cutt's way: the rat trap. He heard that anyone who entered the rat trap did not come back the same. In prison there is a code, and everybody knows the code. No snitchin'. The rat trap unleashes hell on prisoners but Cutt is desperate. One day without affiliation is a nightmare. Jealousy and envy get the most of people and gangstas are no different. Cutt is jealous of the new power Rax wields in prison by virtue of joining The CG, and he's envious of how easy it was for Kid Rax to reinvent himself from a baby gangsta to Raxx OG, hardened criminal down with the most notorious prison gang in the Southwest.

Once Cutt displays a willingness to talk, things move quickly. The District Attorney arranges for a meeting in the rat trap when Cutt's lawyer, Mr. Dublay, intervenes, citing Cutt's safety, as well as the value of the information he will provide, and negotiates a private meeting in the prison library which will be closed for the duration of the meeting. The DA has a hard-on for 2T and agrees to the demands hoping to extract as much info as he can. Turn-a-cutt again makes it clear to Mr. Dublay that his cooperation is based solely on secrecy. Yet when the day comes, despite Cutt feeling confident in what he's about to do, the CO marches him straight into the rat trap.

"What the fuck!! I thought we had a deal, man!!"

"We don't make deals with convicts," says the warden. "And we don't play fuckin' games!"

"Hey, hold up, I'm not here playin', I got some serious shit to tell you—"

"I really don't give a hoot-nanny what you did. You think talkin' will make everything all hunky-dory? You're a fuckin' felon, scumbag, you have no rights."

Stalling the uptight warden is not an option. Turn-a-cutt is out of time. He now realizes he made a deal with the devil. He's beside himself that he trusted the law to keep their word. Instead hell awaits him. In the big time there is only "get" or "get got." You're either predator or prey. And here was Cutt, quickly dropped into an enclosed glass case of venomous snakes with only one way out: talk.

"It is my understanding you have some information for us."

"Yes sir."

"Well why don't you let us know what you know."

"My lawyer said—"

"Never mind what your lawyer said son! Tell us what we need to know."

"It was the Geranimo kid."

"Yes."

"It was Kid Rax."

"Am I hearing what I think I'm hearing, son? You're saying that Kid Rax shot and killed Geranimo Maestas, and that you were witness, and that you're willing to go on record for this?"

"It's true."

The deal went south. Cutt didn't get the release he wanted and the time they agreed to take off his sentence for cooperation didn't equal the danger of them marching him in and out of the rat trap. Now Cutt wasn't even sure he'd live to serve out his sentence. As soon as Cutt left the room there was an immediate change in temperament from the other inmates. Felons only enter that room for one reason. The rest of the inmates—especially the CG—not only harassed him but their eyes glowed red, as if demons had been summoned to claim dominion over Cutt's soul. The next day Turn-a-cutt went to chapel. It was the only place that felt safe. He sat with his hand clutching the Bible when a voice came in closely from the seat behind.

"You have a good time in the rat trap, Cutt?"

. . .

Cell blocks turn into the Devil's playground, and therein begins eternal suffering. They swipe his food, test him regularly, and make life a living hell. Cutt—despite rejection from The Conglomerate—is still excommunicated from 2T officially, and unceremoniously.

Although coming clean about Kid Rax murdering Mo cleared his conscience, his body and mind were subject to the torture of both the CG and The State. Prison guards complained about constantly having to separate him from the other inmates. To them, it felt like they were protecting him. Eventually the warden got fed up with the complaints and decided to ship him off. Word of his pending transport is kept secret and they move swiftly to ship him out.

* * *

They escort Turn-a-cutt to the bus while everyone is in the yard. It doesn't matter who's there; white, black, brown, gang or none, they can't help but notice this special occurrence and line up at the tall metal fence bangin' and cussin', threatening Cutt as he boards the bus. He faces forward, doing his best to ignore them.

Turn-a-cutt doesn't know where they're transporting him and doesn't have a clue of how long he'll be on the bus. He figures they'll transport him to another Colorado prison. They lock him down. Cutt realizes that he is their only passenger. One dejected prisoner. One guard facing Cutt with his hand on his shotgun. And one bus driver.

. . .

Eleven hours they drive. Turn-a-cutt falls asleep and wakes up facing a facility in the desert. It's Texas, The Lone Star State. Cutt ponders the entirety of his life, especially the night Kid Rax killed Geranimo. In less than a year from Mo's murder, Turn-a-cutt turned from gangsta to informant, and predator to prey. Yet something significant comes out of Cutt's confession. Mo's family now knows for sure who pulled the trigger, and Kid Rax, or Raxx OG, or whatever pseudonym he takes, can no longer run from justice.

THE NO 'MO VIOLENCE MOVEMENT

THE VIOLENT LOSS OF LIFE is always tragic. When we experience the loss of young lives within our communities, everyone shares in the grieving process and thus, most want to act for change. Sometimes change happens on a political level. An elected public official states, "We have to do something to end the violence in our neighborhood," and that is how a plan, a bill and general awareness begins. These initiatives are normal in urbanized areas. To those living in the city, this noble reaction is viewed as honorable. And elected officials at their highest degree are just that, honorable. But other movements can be more organic, more community-based, organized with love and purpose.

There are times when grief is relentlessly pulverizing, attacking constantly, maliciously, creating a hole so deep and immeasurable—like the loss of a son to violence—where the mind, body and soul transform into utter survival mode. The hole oneself feels cannot be ignored, it cannot be filled, but sometimes service in the name of our dearly departed can help, can heal, and most of all, can bring back a feeling of hope. Yet the transformative nature of such acts is not for the weak-hearted. Only the wisest, strongest, most intuitive individuals possess this alchemy of servitude. Cathy Maestas lost part of her heart that fateful day her son was murdered, but over time she learned to cope. Her servitude runs parallel with healing, and slowly, she learned how to smile again. But what also helped her heal was doing the unthinkable. Doing what most family members of violence victims cannot do. She did what preachers preach about but most cannot find the courage within themselves to do: she forgave Mo's killer.

In dealing with tragedy Cathy assumed the role of leader. One can say leadership is a quality she possessed all her life, but due to the busyness of that life, a quality she did not get to exercise enough. Natural-born leaders always find their calling, and this time, balancing the weight and burden of leadership was the only thing that made sense in Cathy's world.

As strong as any life coach, more wisdom than scholars, with speech powerful enough to move mountains, this is what Cathy metamorphosed into during the years following Mo's murder. Her calling became crystal clear. Although Mo's love, passion and talent were basketball, it isn't Cathy's forte. Sure, she knew how to cheer, champion, and congratulate Mo's basketball life, but for her to get involved with anything related to basketball would be unnatural. There were glory days of her own that for years she held under her speech. Buried behind her love for her family, but once upon a time, it was as natural and instinctive as her own breath. In extreme cases of grief, we go back to what we know, like starting from scratch per se. Not necessarily a new beginning but for Cathy a resurrection, a rejuvenation, a rectified and sanctified journey back to the essence.

Cathy is still raising Ray Ray and La La. She had to be both mother and big brother to them in Mo's wake. The toughest times, when Cathy was struggling to go on, when she stole moments crying herself to sleep, she immediately came back to motherhood. She had to, that's what mothers do. But you see the dynamic of why it is so hard for mothers to grieve. It's because they still have to be mom, while constantly being asked if they are okay, when really, they just need some time to process, to mourn, to come around to faith that everything is going to be okay. Ray Ray and La La were also trying to make sense of what happened, how they lost big brother Mo—their protector—the one they looked up to in this life. Cathy couldn't replace Mo, nor did she try, and she didn't deprive them of motherly love. She gave them all of her. Her laugh, her smile, her hugs, and her undying devotion. Committed to letting them know that they must move on. Always remember Mo, but don't let his passing guilt them into not trying to make it. She encouraged them to bring Mo's memory with them wherever they went, to keep the torch burning, to keep Mo's spirit alive. Yes, Cathy said all the right things, and she believed in what she said. The Nahautl say be impeccable with your word and her intent was pure. It had to be, in this tumultuous time after Mo's murder, she had to guide her other kids to safety.

Cathy built her courage again and let them fly on their own, while always being available to them. Then there was this calling. This urging from her navel that propelled her forward. She felt it intuitively, reclaiming her own Native ability to connect with the beyond. There was never a moment's pause, she felt it and it was time to go. And what was so great about this new sanctity was that it was Cathy's connection to Aztlan. When she was a youth, Cathy proudly attended the first incantation of Escuela Tlatelolco, the school and learning center envisioned by Rodolfo "Corky" Gonzalez. Aptly named, the last stand of the Mexica people against the Spaniards was at Tlatelolco. About Escuela Tlatelolco, it was said, "It was very steeped in our history, our heritage, our indigenous spirituality of this hemisphere that predates any discovery."

During her time at Escuela Tlatelolco, Cathy learned about the importance of Ballet Folklórico, and how it connects us to our celebrated history. Yet despite the monuments and murals dedicated to Aztlan in Denver, Colorado, Ballet Folklórico was almost forgotten about in our neighborhoods. Ballet Folklórico traces its roots to before 1521—and The Siege of Tenochtitlan—and is another vital link to our heritage. The Spaniards tried to eradicate these danzas. Thankfully, to the people, to our dancing peoples, they were unsuccessful.

With the help and guidance of some old friends, Deb and Al Sena, Cathy took ownership of their Ballet Folklórico group and would transform it into the No 'Mo Violence Cultural Dance Group. A call to action like the horn from a conch shell. Cathy soon galvanized into the roles of mentor, teacher, leader—or dare I say, curandera—and time was not wasted worrying about what people thought. She passed on what was second nature to her: traditional Mexican dancing. She didn't fret about time, instead, she created time to uplift young latinas and latinos, to teach them about Mo's tragic death and how to use that same alchemy contained within themselves to springboard his tragic passing into triumph.

HOW DID THE NAME COME TO BE? Well, what's in a name? And how can we honor someone rightfully? It's the youth who conjured the name Cathy would affix to Mo's movement. Students from Manual High School would summon the testament known as No 'Mo Violence. And who should know but them? Remember, not parallel to gang culture, but within gang culture. The slogan is catchy, but the concept was genius in that it allows for multiple activities—and all in Mo's name—under one unifying umbrella. Think about Civic buildings. Most have noteworthy dedications on a plaque near the entrance. Unfortunately, those dedications are often forgotten. Not so was the case with Cathy's movement, that wouldn't be good enough for Mo's memory, to have some arbitrary name that people forgot about, nope. Her movement hit the nail on the head: No "Mo" Violence. The No 'Mo Violence movement was soon found in The Rocky Mountain News, The Denver Post, La Voz, local television, banners inside schools, flyers taped onto poles within Auraria Campus and push-pinned to the wall at Chubby's, Aztlan, Ashland and St. Charles Recreation Centers, Hip Hop venues, art galleries and City Hall. The movement defied categorization. It grew tentacles, morphing into Ballet Folklórico, a play, 3 on 3 Basketball Tournaments and the El Grito celebration. No "Mo" Violence sponsored community events, food banks and churches. The love Cathy had for Mo was spread to all children to assure this tragedy never happened to another. She did all this so your kids could believe. Imagine the sacrifice it took, every day she saw Mo's face before she fell asleep but woke up the next morning and went to work inspiring your children. Teaching them, molding them, accepting them, validating them.

BECAUSE THE KIDS OF MANUAL HIGH SCHOOL also navigated these tumultuous streets, through No 'Mo Violence they gave Mo's memory the ultimate gift: The gift of remembrance. Their testament is embedded with the code and the code speaks to us from the past. Mo's name intertwined with the word violence is to remind us that violence is senseless. Our true nature is to love one another: "Check the verse in the bible says man should never covet/but in your life you put nothin' above it/you seem to love it."* This is what happened to us. Because we covet material goods, we devalue life. And Mo's life was one of the brightest lives, shining like the brightest star in the cosmos. The testament of No 'Mo Violence means that we can't run from the reality, the life, the death, the potential, the heartache, the joy, the sadness, the pain, the memory or the essence. These truths and emotions are alive within the movement. We are the movement, just like Mo is the movement. The movement teaches us metaphysical truths: Shooting your brother is like shooting yourself. You commit a sin against them and you. There is no reprieve from this truth. The No 'Mo Violence Movement is a mirror, every time another youth goes down it's because we forget this truth and run away from love. It's the constant struggle of duality vs. Oneness.

Cathy Maestas has beat the streets for twenty-five years and is still goin'. Ray Ray Maestas has beat the streets for twenty-five years, La La has beat the streets for twenty-five and still counting. This is an organic movement. A heartquake: Ollin. But the name is key. You cannot speak No 'Mo Violence without saying Mo's name because the youth saved his name. They were prophetic. They were soothsayers. Through No 'Mo Violence generations of kids have learned how to dance. They have learned celebration; they have learned the alchemy of turning a negative to a positive. (And it's all good!)

People stop in awe when they see the No 'Mo Violence's Cultural Dance Group. Clad in white dresses with Mexica patterns, these young women and men put on a show for the culture and for the movement. Their grace exemplifies Mo's memory. Geranimo Maestas is Denver. Mo is the remembrance of the best things about us because he lived life fully. I watch Cathy's undying devotion to her son, to his memory, to all of us. She does it all: Mother, leader, teacher, mentor, and friend. She never had a lot of money but the things she does have are faith, family, belief, love, and God. It's amazing to witness what she has accomplished after everything she has been through. To hear her say it, she gives credit to the essence, the divine, "I'm blessed mijo, I've devoted my life to my Lord and Savior Jesus Christ."

ALAMEDA SQUARE

It's the year 2000 and I'm consumed with creating Hip Hop, earning a reputation as a fierce lyricist (thanks to DJ Chonz and my brothers Eric and Eddie blanketing the North Side with my first outing, "Everyone Knows.") and hitting every Hip Hop event in the city. During the day I double as a responsible young father and I enjoy my occupation: driving buses for the Denver Public Schools. A split-shift allows me to work on music in the afternoon—and alone—while my mother is at work and my brothers are at school.

My route includes Rishel Middle School. I pick up my kids from the projects on 12th and Irving Street. They average 65-70 kids, three to a seat, and let me tell you, that's a heck of a lot of children moving in a confined tube at varied speeds. Dips in the street make the rear end wobble like a teeter-totter.

After my kids are dropped off, I post up by the baseball field with the other buses. We have a layover there and chill for a minute before heading back to base. Sometimes I rap with the other drivers but mostly I head out on foot to Alameda Square which is adjacent to Rishel's baseball field. Deep in the corner of the square is a Taqueria where I order a chorizo breakfast burrito and a Coke. The other morning, I was waiting for my order and saw a flyer for a Hip Hop jam celebrating all four elements of the culture. It was at another venue in the Square, and a mere twenty paces from the Taqueria. There was to be a rap battle, a B-Boy battle—both individual and crew—DJ sets, graff pieces on display and multiple features. The event would be hosted by Dent, an emcee I had met at a party around the way and a freestyle aficionado. I knew what he could do because I had witnessed him and Afrikan Sam in a cypher at that same party. They did this incredible walkie talkie impression where they would bounce back and forth off each other, mimicking the white noise of CB radio transmissions before lyrics were dispersed. I snagged a copy of the flyer and knew I had to be there.

It's the night of the jam, but Noel Z. is out with his girl and my brothers are busy getting lifted, so I guess I'm heading solo shot. The $10 cover charge burns a whole in my pocket but the boomin' bass gets my blood pumping again.

The jam is like a who's who of the Colorado Hip Hop scene. Dent is in rare form, keeping the mood festive with his jokes and focusing the attention of the crowd on the next performance that's in store, even doing a bit of freestyling himself. Adict, creator and host of Basementalism Radio 1190 is here, forever recruiting talent to interview on his program based in CU Boulder's basement, which broadcasts every Saturday from 4pm-7pm throughout the Front Range. Alongside Dent on stage, Stro from The Procussions is encased in the middle of an illustrious 12-piece drum set, drumming along with some of the songs for the breakers and DJ's and trust me, it is a sight—and sound—to behold. Mr. J and Rez, the other members of The Procussions are here to round out the unit, and their group's performance blows the minds of the crowd. Battle-rapping royalty Black Pegasus and Mic Jones are here as well as a young and hungry Spoke In Wordz. Can't forget about conscious head Saamir and Fly Jedi, who are busy passing out promotional CD's to any and everybody. Brown Bombas and Amadeo are passing out flyers too, they have a jam coming up soon that's gonna be ill.

When the B-Boy feature jumps off I'm in line for a brew, so I miss the first homie's name and part of his feature. I return to the spot overlooking the floor and have a wood-tipped Swisher intertwined in the same hand I clutch my Newcastle with. Meanwhile, Dent is busy keeping the focus of the room on the B-Boys in the center of the jam on the duct-taped linoleum.

Lo and behold there's this kid breakin' like his life depends on it, using every square inch of the linoleum, head and shoulders a better dancer than all the breakers I had seen. Suspended in air at once then winding the next. I don't recognize this dancer, but he embodies cohesiveness, rhythm, and motion. Not like the other wannabe's who at a glance, one can tell that in their head they're counting steps. No sir, you can tell this kid feels the music, embodies the music, as opposed to acting as marionette to the music. This kid and Hip Hop are complementarians of the highest form. He is hand-jumping—as in jumping on his hands! The crowd erupts in favor of this kid puttin' it down and workin' hard. Then comes the mind-numbing headspin. First medium speed, then fast, then slow. How he do that! For magicians like this, gravity does not exist.

After the feature, they announced the B-Boy's name again to roaring applause: "Give it up for the world renowned, and Denver Native: Ray Ray Maestas!" What?! It can't be. And he's not even battling, he was so dope, he is the feature. I follow him through the crowd and wait until every B-Boy in the jam gives him his propers, then I make my move.

I roll up on him with a huge smile across my face. Surely he will recognize me, right? But it's awkward because I haven't seen him in so long. I don't even know if I should call him Ray Ray or if he will correct me. Just like Mo, he stands tall, exuding pride and confidence.

"Ray Ray."

"Gabe? Hey!" (A dap followed by a hug.)

"What's up brother?! That shit you did was DOPE!! How you been?"

"Oh, thank you. I been good brother, real good. I've been blessed, traveling all around the world because of my dancing. I actually just got back yesterday from Doha, Qatar. I been to Japan, Shanghai, all over."

"That's amazing, man! It's so good to see you."

"You too. How you doin'?"

"I'm tryin' to do the same thing you're doing, man. I got a CD out and it's getting a little buzz."

"You rap?"

"Yeah, man. I used to bump all that MTV shit before Mo introduced me to Hip Hop and now, I can't see doin' anything else. He showed me the way."

"Showed us the way."

"Amen to that, brother. Damn, I still miss him."

"I miss him, too."

"What's it been, like 7 years?"

"Yeah, since the funeral."

Our heads bow down and we pause.

". . . How is everybody?"

"My mom's been staying strong and keeping busy with No 'Mo Violence and all, and La's got kids now."

"That's crazy! But I'm glad they're doing their thing, though. Sounds like their doin' good."

"They are—hey, I gotta bounce soon but we should connect."

"No doubt, bro, let me get your number."

"Alright, bet."

* * *

Nothing is trivial. Not the staircase descending to the jam nor the heavy hitters in the venue. Ray Ray and I share the same root, and despite not communicating for years, we are both living and breathing Hip Hop. For us, there is no other truth.

Ray Maestas was doing what he loved, and I saw the pride in his face as he told me about his travels. He put in the work and through countless hours of practice, scaled the mountaintop. I'm hoping to follow suit, trying to reach my own pinnacle, and creeping on a come up.

If only Mo could see us now.

WORLD RENOWN

DYSLEXIA IS A NEUROLOGICAL DISORDER that involves difficulty in processing letters and language. Most importantly, when people suffer from dyslexia, they lack confidence. Learning gives you wings, but those with dyslexia feel grounded, the gravitational pull of the disorder limits their movement. Ray Ray experienced self-doubt early in life due to the disorder. Unlike the natural reaction of a basketball game upon the street top, Ray Ray's feet perspired profusely during school, the extreme humidity within his Pro Keds cascading into pools of sweat. His socks stayed dry until 9:30am, which is when Ray Ray's teacher, Mrs. Foote, would begin her lesson in Reading and Comprehension. Before a single bead of sweat landed on his shirt collar, Ray Ray's socks and shoes were drenched.

Ray Ray tied his shoes as tight as possible, figuring that if no air could escape, then no one would smell the funk from his feet. He tied them so tight the shoestrings became as thin as fishing line, and the loops from the knots dragged on the floor. He kicked his shoes on the porch afterschool, but it took all night for the sneakers to dry. Eventually, Ray Ray adjusted to putting on damp sneakers the next learning day. One whiff of his shoes and his mom would march him off to the tub to wash his feet. Ray Ray took so many talcum powder foot baths that his feet turned white. Cathy then pulled enough money together to buy Ray Ray a new pair of kicks. New sneakers would fix this mess, right? The sneakers were ruined in a day. Ray Ray cowered inside. He couldn't understand how other kids saw the letters much less interpreted them enough to read a sentence. The word dad looked like bab, and spelling tests were just times when Ray Ray scribbled down symbols he couldn't comprehend. Once, he turned in an empty sheet of paper and Mrs. Foote lectured him about the profundity of trying, but the act of trying became another weight around his neck, and the heat generated within his shoes during tests was enough to melt steel.

There were times when young Ray Ray was pushed to his limits, and because he desired Mo's approval, the hazing he endured was worth the reward. One day, he followed Mo, Pablo and I to my house. Although it was a straight shot down Quieto Court and a quick left on 44th to Quivas, Mo took a detour and started up toward Smedley. Once we emerged from the alley onto 42nd we sprinted from Ray Ray leaving him far behind. Mo started kickin' those Jordans and we followed suit. We stopped at the end of the block to turn around and wait for Ray Ray's head to come popping around the corner. Once Mo caught a glimpse of Ray Ray we sprinted to the next block. The game continued like this around Smedley's school grounds then onto Chaffee Park. Ray Ray was oblivious of the winos lurking in the bushes yet here he was, a mere 5 years old, curious and gullible and running over that tall, slicked grass. We slid into the bathroom then doubled-back. "Mo!" Ray Ray shouted into the bathroom while we were cloaked in the bushes. Unrelenting, we took off again while Ray Ray stood hot on our trail. He never batted an eye and wore a smile the whole time. Ray Ray thought this was a game rather than a test. No teacher to worry about, no letters to decipher and none of the other kids' pointed laughs.

Ray Ray finally reached us at my house. My brothers, Eric and Eddie, who were the same age as Ray Ray, were playing outside. The guys thought it would be cool to introduce Ray Ray to the twins and his eyes lit up when he saw them. He looked at Mo then looked at the twins again. How can these two look exactly alike? "Why don't you guys show Ray Ray your toys?" I told my brothers, and their heads went about the lawn in unison searching for items. They were in the age of Tonka trucks and stuff, but the guys and I had something better to worry about: that pale orange dot.

The Earth loves non-stop dribbling. In winter, if the concrete was free of ice, the dribbling continued. Even over dead leaves, on Halloween, on Easter: Reverence had to be paid to basketball. After multiple games of 21, we drank from the hose and it was almost time to head back to Mo's. I said something awful to my brothers and as Ray Ray turned around fists were flying. Eric and Eddie were fighting each other, amplifying their adolescent battle cries and using wrestling moves in between. Mo turned to Ray Ray, who was enjoying the show, comfortable that he didn't have to step in between this sibling rivalry, for he preferred running us down to throwin' blows.

Eric and Eddie broke their melee for a sec, and that's when Mo turned to his little brother and said, "Okay, Ray Ray, now it's your turn." Ray Ray looked at Mo with a big smile. A funny joke, big brother is always playin', right? Mo looked back at Ray Ray with a straight face and serious demeanor. All that runnin' and chasin' for another test, and a violent one at that. Ray Ray knew what he had to do because Mo called the shots. He didn't want to risk not being invited on future excursions. Ray Ray looked at the space in the lawn occupied by the twins as if it were a plank leading to the ocean. He stepped onto the lawn with hands deep in his pockets. "You guys are gonna have to decide who's gonna fight," I said, again harping on my brothers. Eddie then mashed Eric in the face and stood in front of Ray Ray. Bragging rights were at stake for a seat at the table; future generations to be decided. The Denver sun shone perfectly. Pablo was smiling, eyes bulging wondering who would land the first blow. Suddenly, Mo threw his hands in the air and ran between Ray Ray and Eddie. "Wait, wait, wait, wait, wait!" Mo proclaimed with the tact of a boxing ring judge. "You guys don't have to do this, we're just playin'."

Mo was flattered, if not slightly terrified at the level of loyalty our younger brothers exhibited that day. We were familiar with calling the shots, comfortable setting precedent, and wielding universes to our liking. Eric, Eddie and Ray Ray were eager to do it, to prove to their elders that they were cool. The best part was that Pablo loved the fight. There wasn't a winner, just a whole lot of swingin' and low hitting percentages but it was funny as hell. The next time we tried staging these fights, my mom caught us red-handed and everyone was in trouble. The screen door banged shut as we left the house, walking by Eric and Eddie without saying goodbye, Ray Ray tailing behind, but we didn't run from him this time.

Despite fun days like these Ray Ray had a tumultuous upbringing with challenges and setbacks. After Mo's murder, heartbreak set in, but sometimes those with the hardest path reach the mountaintop. The grind was normal life for Ray Ray. His father was in and out of jail, yet his mother believed in him. Mothers are like that, trusting. Belief can make a muthafucker do the impossible, the improbable. Visions Ray Ray had were perceptive, 20/20 visuals that transported him to the past. He was shown Mo's all-black outfit with the gleam of pristine white Air Jordans which accentuated Mo's cabbage patch. "This was the path," Ray Ray concluded. Not an easy path. Not one accepted by society or one that brings much money. But one that is about passion. Ray Ray had that in droves.

This white shoes/black pants illusion planted a seed in Ray Ray's mind. And to the bassline of Special Ed's "I Got It Made"

Mo would dance: 1, 2, kick 1, 2 kick, then stand on one leg while it swiveled, kicking out with the other leg as an anchor to keep the opposite foot moving. Ray Ray remembered the dedication Mo showed him when he needed support. When Ray Ray had to study Psalms and other passages for his first communion, it was Mo who would read to him.

Ray Ray dropped out of school to follow his dream. He knew he would have to travel and commune with, and study under, the elite. Hip Hop culture is just that, a culture. And a B-Boy's realm is even more cutthroat, because mentors do not take on just any students. Learners must possess the total package. A love, willingness, skill, work-ethic, humbleness, and sometimes geography, for he would have to go were the B-Boy's were. "Have Love, Will Travel," was Ray-Ray's cardboard sign he wore on his sleeve. No dancer would out-work him, no B-Boy could claim geographical advantage over his heart, and his alchemy was to transform life's greatest obstacles into gems.

The discipline of breakin' spilled over into other key aspects of Ray Ray's life. Discipline would be needed to read. Ray Ray wanted to know what was in these pages of books. He wanted to use his library card on books for once instead of VHS movies. He yearned for what many of us take for granted, the gift of reading. To start at the beginning—as an adult—is not only hard, but also humbling. Hell, it's damn near embarrassing. Ray Ray didn't care who looked or laughed or jabbed or commented. It was his destiny to read books. This was the Zen approach that alluded him all his life. He was familiar with the Yoga discipline. Physicality and sweat. Body gyrations and leaps and lunges and most magnificently of all, head spins.

Everybody remembers "Hooked on Phonics." It was a very productive program. Kids in the '80s were relentless, and through the '90s it didn't change. Kids made fun of you if you were hooked on phonics. Pop culture and comedians took hold of the phenomenon known as hooked on phonics and were relentless. They called it Hooked on Stupid. But words are phonetic, and Ray Ray was serious as a heart attack. He had traveled the world in his breakin' shoes with a never say die mentality, and now he had to coalesce it into letter A. The postcards he sent to his mom from around the world were statements of his winning. And everybody likes a winner.

The four elements of Hip Hop are deejayin, emceein, b-boyin, and graffiti art. Ray Ray partook in all and mastered one, training with the late, great Gary Kendell, a key figure of the Jabbawockeez. You can find Ray Ray on YouTube, either in a B-Boy Battle or scaling a mountain with one hand, or flash-mobbing the 16th Street Mall bus in downtown Denver. It's in his heart, and Mo provided the spark.

LOST & FORGOTTEN

MOVEMENTS ARE RARELY RESERVED for the living. No movement was created for Estevan and yet, Estevan would feel uneasy for the rest of his life. Tortured continuously, caught between seeing the world through his own eyes and seeing the world through the eyes of those who loved Mo, Estevan observed how people did their best to honor Mo's life.

Secretly he thought, maybe Mo was the one in a better place, for he would not have to suffer through this life wounded, broken and behind the eight ball for what seemed like an eternity. Estevan was the one the paramedics saved. The one they would revive and bring back to life. "We couldn't save them both . . ."

Estevan spent weeks in bouts of depression that got worse when mixed with alcohol. He didn't possess the gifts and talents that Mo had, none of us did. Nevertheless, he had what Mo didn't have after the shooting: a future. And this future should have meant that he rejoices in being alive, to feel euphoric to wake each and every day, and to be free from the nightmares. But every breath became a burden for Estevan. The open-air Denver breeze flowed through his nostrils into lifeless lungs and positivity never bloomed in his being again. His heart stoically pumping unassuming blood into unwarranted veins. "Ifs and buts, candy and nuts," people would say.

"How can I think such things?" Estevan thought, punishing himself. Thoughts that seemed so callous in nature, especially to those who championed Mo's legacy. Estevan's silence became a self-made purgatory. He still had nightmares and flashbacks of the incident, but he also punished himself for feeling sorry for himself. He loved Mo too—looked up to him—yet as the years rolled by Estevan would self-induce guilt upon himself to the highest degree. The years hardened his soul, ate at his insides and he became a recluse.

Make no mistake there were two victims that fateful night, one dead, the other barely breathing. A remnant of chaos like residue from a shotgun.

STAKES IS HIGH

A FAMOUS DENVER ATHLETE IS MURDERED.

It's New Year's Day, January 1, 2007. Today we enter a new environment. An environment where even the untouchables are now touchable. "How did we get here?" newspaper reporters and newscasters ponder, but the people in the streets already know. Today, both the Broncos and Denver suburbanites catch up to the reality in the streets. TwentySeven was a football phenom with a budding career growing in money and success. The town fell in love with this man. His smile, his congeniality, and most of all, his competitiveness. Sports heroes are always idolized in Denver. [Even if they are significantly ahead of their time, à la Mahmoud Abdul-Rauf.]

Just a decade earlier, Colorado was stage to the 24-hour news cycle, where the world watched the eventual unsolved murder of a child beauty pageant contestant. Although it was the Boulder Police Department, and the city of Boulder for that matter, (once described as four-square miles surrounded by reality) the botched investigation and unsolved murder case virtually left all police departments in Colorado—by mere association—at a disadvantage in the public's opinion of their competence to see high-profile cases through to a conviction. That said, everything was on the line for this one. A call comes in from Mayor Hicken-looper's office to the chief of police: "All hands-on deck."

* * *

They walk through those double-paned doors with a common color in their wares. Black Chuck's, black sweatshirts, and black Nike's. But we are blind. Blind to any other color but green. (Cream! Dollar dollar bill y'all!) We look the other way in desperation, have their comps ready as they walk through the door. We know they play at The Lodge and Ameristar, but they are average players there. We offer *exclusivity*.

Our table games operation is struggling. We're the new kids on the block. No hotel and no buffet, and no incentive to lose your money to us. Due to our disjointed training and wearisome drop, our emphasis on Title 31 compliance was shotty at best. And the only reason someone would want to evade Title 31 is for the purpose of money laundering, funneling cash from illegal activities into pure, fresh, untraceable, and legal C-Notes.

* * *

Sitting 8,043 feet in elevation, Black Hawk is an old mining town that was rejuvenated in the early '90s by limited-stakes gambling. At that elevation you can grab a piece of cumulus if you want to. Saloons from the gold rush days were refurbished into twenty casinos cut into the side of a mountain and there you have the city of Black Hawk. Historic plaques lace the miniscule town and talk about pioneers moving westward, but no vestiges remain of the natives who were slaughtered to make the push. Limited stakes gambling meant that table games in Colorado held a maximum of only $5, which they got around creatively with games like Streak Blackjack, a game that allowed players to—within the strict rules of limited stakes—bet a total of $30 each round. But regardless of these ingenious inventions exploiting loopholes in Colorado's rules, the climate of restriction and regulation scared many would be conglomerate suitors. Harrah's Entertainment had opened a few casinos when the town went live in 1991 but quickly exited due to the constriction, as did Harvey's, including their highly touted and widely promoted spokesperson: Bill Cosby. From its inception, Black Hawk always had a downside in terms of obstacles to their business, and when you're trying to wield huge profits, limited stakes was a begrudged governor. Yet a bigger obstacle was location. Being an hour drive from Denver was extremely unfortunate, because if people wanted to gamble, they would have to make a day of it.

* * *

Just yesterday, the Denver Broncos finished their season on the last day of 2006 with a loss, finishing with a disappointing 8-8 record. After the game, TwentySeven and a few other players went to a party hosted by a couple of Denver Nuggets players. Altercations persisted throughout the night although none were taken seriously by the high-class brass of athletes in the room. Unknowingly, the Broncos and Nuggets were rubbing shoulders with the shot-callers of Denver's gang culture. High-profile parties always bring out the criminal element, but the problem is, that while most athletes feel invincible when on the field, they make the crucial—sometimes deadly—mistake of thinking they are invincible inside the club too. Street gangs do not take this attitude lightly, no matter how big a star athlete may be. You better show respect to their forum. Or else.

* * *

We have an overreaching habit to offer up the house to anyone gambling a few thousand dollars; that's how desperate we are. But they're friendly. Knowledgeable to the game of Craps yet trying to get familiarized quickly to its complicated layout. I can't blame them, with real money on the line and dice dealers yelling "Seven Out" frequently, they do their best to catch up.

We continue stuffing hundreds in the box, and despite our new clientele's winning streak, Mohawk Casino's General Manager, repeatedly emphasizes the importance of having the *action*, and that eventually, the tides will swing in our favor. They have to, all casino games are favored toward the house.

* * *

The casinos in Black Hawk are separated by Main Street, a long and windy road, sometimes snowy, sometimes icy, but always paved with gold. Amendments and initiatives to raise the stakes were brought up each election cycle, usually though, they were crushed by the opposition. Naysayers consistently painted pictures of poverty-stricken, gambling-addicted, and crime-infested scenarios to scare even the most conservative of voters. Colorado was meant to be pure, and nothing was purer—and American—than limited stakes gambling. That is until Amendment 50, and the 2008 election.

Meant to be a shot in the arm for a failing industry, Amendment 50 would bring Craps, Roulette, and higher stakes. $100 to be exact, and on each individual bet, meaning you could bet $100 any way to the number on Roulette, or go $100 on the line with $100 odds on Craps. That's quite the payoff, and due to Amendment 50, casino profits were projected to increase a hundredfold.

Steph and I were living in Vegas at the time, getting extremely homesick, and basically gambled on gambling, moving back to town before the historic vote. We figured that if it passed, I would be at the right place and the right time with knowledge of both Craps and Roulette. As constructed, the town was still anchored by Blackjack and its ancillary games, followed by a couple of offshoot Texas variations. If Amendment 50 didn't pass, I would have to be okay with pumping cards on Streak Blackjack beside a piece of Blarney Stone inside Fitzgerald's Casino. But we couldn't lose, ALL OUR MONEY WAS ON 50.

* * *

Fans demand justice for murdered celebrities, and even those in City Hall were fanatics of the Denver Broncos. The bottom line was, we couldn't have a pro athlete—a Denver Bronco no less—slain in our streets. The general public is intrigued by who was evil enough to do it, knowing that Police Departments wish to solve such rare cases because often times, the world may be watching. Memorials to honor the slain star were conducted. None more heart-wrenching then watching TwentySeven's jersey ascend to the beloved Ring of Fame around Mile High Stadium. This became the climate in late 2007, and the Denver Broncos dedicated their 2007-2008 season to the memory of

TwentySeven. Unfortunately, by the end of 2008 and through the first half of 2009, news of the investigation trickles into nothing.

* * *

Before I began applying to casinos in Black Hawk, I had only visited the town once before—as a minor—as my dad and Grandma Gloria were jonesing so bad they took me on one of their gambling adventures. Riding up the switchbacks of the canyon through the Rocky Mountains they prepped me on the proper etiquette for a minor accompanying an adult in the casino, which led me to believe that I was not the only minor or cousin they hauled up there. The rules were basically shut up and don't touch shit, which I was extremely confident I could handle. When we entered the casinos doors, I was astonished by the mobs of people rushing to lose their money and by the runneth over plastic cups my grandmother was holding, I hadn't dreamed of that many nickels before! These were the glory days of Black Hawk everybody reminisced about. This was before the smoking ban, which banned all smoking in casinos, basically cutting business in half because the smokers left in protest and never came back.

But Amendment 50 was legislative rejuvenation, and best of all, backed by a failsafe: the profits generated from all Craps and Roulette tables would be siphoned to fund community colleges across the front range. This is politics 101, greedy casino companies: bad, greedy casino companies funding education: good. Amendment 50 passed, and I was hired as Table Games Manager for Mohawk Casino.

Don was my first employee. I hired him on the spot. I immediately knew what I could expect from him. He talked me up in the interview. Not about him, about me, about how he could be my right-hand man, the enforcer if you will, my extended muscle that would enforce the department's policy and procedures when I wasn't there.

* * *

In his first two seasons, TwentySeven amassed six interceptions and two defensive touchdowns, spectacular numbers for any cornerback at any stage of their career.

Mo's 5A numbers were buried in the back page of the sports section. To hear Mo tell it, he put 50 on the opposition when he played against Machebeuf. Cathy keeps Mo's trophies on her mantle.

* * *

"If a woman can make some good brown gravy, I'm hers for life," said Don, who was rubbing his belly and beaming, for he had had a great two months with Sharon and was preparing for her to move in with him. Sharon was an astrologer and owned a shop down in Thornton on Washington Street. When I met Sharon, she promised me and Steph discounts on readings and we were curious enough to go. Steph went first and I waited out in the car during the reading and she eventually came out flaunting a TDK cassette and smile. She soon filled me in on the details, direct signs from the cosmos which correlated to her imminent future. Because of Steph's profound experience, and some egging-on by Don, I decided to give it a try as well. This time I went solo shot, waiting behind the beaded doorway wondering what details would be revealed to me from the universe. It started out great, but then Sharon saw something misbehaving in the cards and took a deep breath before delivering the news. All she said was that "evil was lurking."

* * *

Violence begets violence. Just like Mo, TwentySeven was taken too soon from those who loved him most, and another mother was left without her son. But the public never rallied on Mo's side for justice. Only one person, Cathy Maestas, fought for Mo's justice, and that his memory lived on. As TwentySeven would be enshrined the following season, Mo's likeness still hadn't appeared anywhere in the Denver Parks & Recreation, much less St. Charles Recreation Center, though Cathy lobbied constantly for it. The Denver Parks & Recreation just didn't have the money. (It was always about the money.)

Mo was murdered for his Denver Broncos coat. Would Mo's dedication to his home team qualify for the Broncos' illustrious Ring of Fame? Was the Denver Broncos organization and players aware of what happened midseason on November 26, 1993? Mo never saw the new Broncos logo, they unveiled it in 1997, the year they won their first Super Bowl. Were Mo alive would he have rocked the new logo? You bet your ass he would've. Proudly. Mo would've loved to see them hoist that trophy too.

In this new era, everyone is still debating the intersection of sports and social justice. But I tell you this, Mo would've been vehemently opposed to the Cleveland Indians' name and likeness, not to mention the Chiefs, Braves, Seminoles, and Blackhawks. Mestizo blood and his knowledge of the plight of indigenous cultures would've landed him right smack dab in the front of the grassroots #NotYourMascot Movement. Mo was murdered for his jacket. Is it the Broncos' fault this happened? No. But his bronzed bust should adorn the entrance just like other Broncos greats. For the town, for the struggle, for the memory, for Mo. We are one. Isn't that the meaning of Broncos Country?

* * *

Although we have 3x4x5x odds, they play $100 on the line with $100 odds, taking advantage of the newly passed maximums for each individual bet. They keep $100 each on the 6 and 8 too. It's hard to beat those with bankrolls, but if the losing streak is long enough, the house always has a chance.

* * *

People liked the burgers at Mohawk Grille, and so they came in for a good burger. Getting away from the stresses of the city was a good time for everyone. You didn't hear any construction or car horns. Just serene weather, clean air and breathtaking views. One day, when the road from Golden was closed, I witnessed a deer crouched in the street because it had been stricken by an automobile. A gentleman went into the middle of the road, cussing at passing traffic and pleading to the deer: "Get up! Get up!" The deer did eventually get up, and it gloriously pranced away despite just having met the bumper of a speeding car. Needless to say, it's different up there.

I met recluse pit bosses, who will never leave the city of Black Hawk for as long as they live. Opposite city dwellers who liked the slow pace of the town. The Colorado Gaming Control Board mirrored the characters depicted from the Nevada Gaming

Control Board in the Motion Picture "Casino," who had cowboy hats and a frontiersmen attitude: *"this is our town, and we allow you to work in it."*

But the push to get these newly approved games up and running wasn't as easy as it sounded, even for huge conglomerates like Ameristar and Jacobs Entertainment. Members of the Colorado Gaming Control Board were so naive that in writing the rules and regulations for Craps, they included the *Fire Bet*—which is a proprietary game—into law.

There was a new marketing campaign every day by one of the casinos to get the word out about 50. Fortune Hills Casino surprised everyone and posted up on a downtown sidewalk with a craps tub, four dealers and some promotional chips. Everybody loves craps, and soon the Front Range will be blasted by marketing.

* * *

One night my swing shift crew had an altercation with the group, and eventually had them removed. Don called me at home later that night to explain the situation. Black Hawk is not a 24-hour town. The doors are shuttered nightly at 2am and last call was a generous 1:40am, sometimes later. But it was only half-passed midnight when Don called security to intervene on his behalf. His premise? Foul language. They were muthafuckin' any and everything. First because they were losing, then they were muthafuckin' Don.

Kicking folks out of casinos is always hard. You never know who you're saying *no* to. Say it to the wrong person and you'll have an all-out war on your hands. Out came Dillon, with his Marshall's tie and all black boots. As a group, they were only down $10,000 at that point, not huge money to be down for them, but Don's strict stance fueled their rage. I don't know if his decision was sound or if he was just tired. Either way, I reviewed the surveillance footage the morning after.

It was inconclusive, and I figured it would be, missing audio is a huge deal. The only thing that saved my crew were the hundreds of cameras that were around, new PTZ's that were installed as a part of our reboot. They also must have realized that we knew their names and addresses—due to them signing up for our rewards program (which wasn't much of a rewards program)—and felt the pinch of the Rocky Mountains, because there are only two routes out of Black Hawk, either through the canyon to Golden or catapulting over Central City to catch I-70. (I don't feel it necessary to mention the third, with its non-railing and treacherous switchbacks, it wouldn't be a good exit for the idea of fleeting.) There was one security supervisor and a security guard. That's it. And the dice dealers had to stay idle on the game through the worst of it.

Dillon said when he told them he called BHPD, that it was the only thing that made them exit. Otherwise, it would have been an interesting night.

* * *

Later that week Steph, Maya, Isaiah, and I were eating dinner when Don called. He was watching the local news and there was an update to TwentySeven's homicide case. They put up a mugshot and it was the same guy he kicked out that night, the de facto leader of the group. He was wanted for TwentySeven's murder, but more importantly—a gangsta from the same gang who murdered Mo sixteen years ago!

"What are the odds?" I thought. One to a hundred? One to a million? The words of Don's astrologer girlfriend, Sharon, siphoned back to my head: Not only lurking evil, but a reminder of pain and loss from the past.

My crew is a bunch of gaming industry veterans that have seen it all, yet when they came in the following night, they were still scared, and feeling like they escaped one. For me, it reinforced the sacrament Mo made to defend himself that night long ago.

DERELICTS OF DIALECT

I'M SPEEDING TO DROP OFF my child support check at the UPS Store on Grant St. When we moved back to Denver, my child support officer and I struck a deal that since I never missed a payment, she would allow me to continue making payments without garnishing my wages. It was six of one, half dozen of the other but the illusion of sending it in without being garnished felt less invasive. Yet one month I arrived to the last day without making a payment and called my officer in a panic, offering to drive my check to her office at the Health & Human Services on 12th & Feds. (She also told me if I was late with one payment, she would begin garnishment.)

The result of that panicked phone call was the guarded secret of the one and only UPS Store—down in Lodo—who will accept child support payments until the very last day of the month. As long as it's in an employee's hand by closing, it will be considered on time. This was welcomed news, for not even the buffer of seven days helped the Post Office deliver my check to its rightful place of collection. Today is my third month in a row of dropping off at the UPS Store. Thankfully, I have a stamp, and dutifully write the Health & Human Services' address on the front of the envelope that my support payment is enclosed in. I'm happy I find a meter a couple blocks away and don't have to double-park. The meter still has time, all I need now is to drop that check. I'm close to the stairs leading to the store when I hear, "Gabe! . . . Oh shit! It's you!" Turning to my right I see Hydro, the homie.

"What up, homie!"

"Hey, how ya been, man?!"

"Good. What you up to? You look like you're going to the UPS Store."

"Yeah, man, I gotta drop off my child support check."

"Oh shit, (dap and snap) you too! I'm dropping off mines too, brother."

I see a check in Hydro's hand and offer to help him out. "You need a envelope, 'Dro?"

"What?! Nah, fuck those envelopes. Yo, straight up, you can just hand 'em a check. I don't fuck with no postage or none of that!"

"No shit? They just take that shit bare bones like that?"

"Fuckin-A!"

"What happened, I ain't seen you in front of Chubby's no more, you ain't slangin' CD's no more, 'Dro?"

"Nah, homie. Shit got deep, some fool broke into my pad and stole all my towers."

"That's fucked up, man."

"Yeah, off to the next grind I guess. I heard the FBI be taking that shit serious now anyway."

"Hey, you seen Pablo? I heard he was back again."

"Yo man, the Iraq war messed with his mind or something. He don't be making beats no more and sometimes he even talks bad about Hip Hop."

"Really?! Why would he do that?"

"I don't know. He says he fought for everyone to have freedom of speech but then hates everyone for having an opinion. I just think he's having a hard time adjusting."

"I'd still like to see him, though. He used to play ball against my friend Mo. They had a nice little rivalry."

"Who's that, now?"

"Ah, you ever heard of Geranimo Maestas, 'Dro? He was the one who got murdered for his jacket in '93."

"Oh yeah, I do remember that, that was cold-blooded man. That was your homie?!"

"Yeah 'Dro, you woulda liked him, he was a real cool dude."

"That's cool man. Hey, I got Pablo's number if you want it."

"Yo man, absolutely!"

* * *

12 Coronas deep in the basement at Pablo's where his equipment looks dusty. It's not a good dust. It's a defiant dust. A permanent pause on the legacy that is Hip Hop. All his Hip Hop posters are removed but for one, Mystikal, a veteran. I'm looking at his equipment going to waste down here. Pablo knows what's running through my mind and he anticipates my question so bad he's salivating. For Pablo, sweet drumbeats were replaced by order of the military.

"What do you think about when Common says on "Respiration" that he's a "veteran of the Cold War?"

"He's full of shit, doggy. The Cold War was not a war."

"Then why do they call it a war if it's not a war?"

"Fuck that doggy! How the fuck are you gonna say some shit like that bro, I fought for the flag!" His eyes are glazed and we're chest to chest.

"Chill, bro, chill. I don't mean no disrespect, bro."

"Don't come in my house sayin' shit like that, doggy."

"But you're the expert on this shit. That's why I'm asking you about it, P."

"You used to rhyme all the time, too, doggy. So you know he's just going for effect."

"But I hear what he's sayin', though. He's sayin' they teach us war from the start. Not to mention the propaganda. It's all game, man. They put us in these public schools and feed us this shit. Like Columbus discovering America and all that."

"Look doggy, ain't no public school put me on tha game. These muthafuckas in the streets is savage homie. I mean yeah, I think Columbus is a puto too, but school is where Mo played his best ball."

"True."

"You didn't go to no college and get no degree, doggy, you read a couple books and think you tha shit. You think you know the pain of losing Mo more than I do? Chale! Get the fuck outta here with that shit, doggy. You're not special."

"I don't think I'm the shit I just think it's all fucked up, man. Fuckin' gangs and shit."

"Hey, I know, doggy." Hands me another Corona.

"I just never dealt with it bro. In '93 Mo got killed. In '95 we had to bury little Juanito. He was only 11 years old, man."

"Hey, we lost soldados too."

"I been watching crazy ass videos on YouTube and shit bro. These conspiracy theory joints—deep as fuck bro. This is my entrada—"

"STOP—Don't say that shit, you sound white when you try to say that shit."

"I'm learnin', though. You can't take that from me."

"You can't be down with the brown just like that."

"Bro, all my grandparents spoke Spanish, it ain't my fault they didn't teach me. I'm your gente whether I speak Spanish or not. And just as you're sayin' that I gotta take you to task. You weren't around after Mo left the North Side. He came and scooped me up and took me to Montbello and the East Side. Mo never saw color, he had friends from all races."

"Look doggy, I traveled around the world two times and I can tell 'ya from experience that brown stays with brown, black stays with black, and white stays with white."

"Fuck that, man, I ain't livin' my life based on the politics of the barracks, and that ain't how Mo lived his life either."

"Hey, that's just the way it is, doggy, you just don't want to admit it."

"That's some New World Order-type shit. They want us to be divided, that's how they keep us controlled, man."

"You're too much of a civilian to even know, doggy. You never been nowhere. Your whole point of view is a Hip Hop point of view."

"Wait a minute, bro. Mo loved Hip Hop . . . He was Hip Hop . . . *is* Hip Hop."

"Doggy, there's barely even any Latinos in Hip Hop."

"What the fuck you mean, barely? I'm the last one you wanna do this with. You know me, P, I repped Psycho Les to the fullest!"

"And muthafuckas still don't care about The Beatnuts."

"Right? I mean Les and Juju produced for everybody. Chi-Ali and Da Youngstas. And what about their own shit? Nobody even puts them top 5 for producers. Cuban Link wasn't even signed when they put him on "Off The Books." Greatest producers never heard."

"Straight up, doggy."

"What about you, P? You had some of the dopest beats in Denver. What happened?"

"I grew up, doggy."

"So you're sayin' Hip Hop isn't grown now? Hip Hop is our foundation, man."

"It's our foundation, but it's not our culture—"

"It is my culture! Bro, what about Cypress, Delinquent Habits, Funkdoobiest, Frost?"

"I'm not gonna give you Frost, doggy, you never bumped that shit back in the day."

"But you know that 'Hey DJ' by Lighter Shade of Brown was my joint!"

"True ... but you'll never be down with the brown."

"So now raza is some type of gang now?" (P cringes from the way I pronounce raza.)

"None of us were ever cool like Mo, doggy. He could be down with everybody. He just had it like that, but that's not us."

"That's for damn sure, man."

"Damn, doggy. He was the one."

"True indeed."

170

THIS IS COMBAT I KNOW

IN THE 1993 FILM, *Meteor Man*, Jeff—the main character played by Robert Townsend—uses his newfound supernatural powers to oust the prominent gang terrorizing his block; a theatrical example of how gangs threatened communities nationwide, and how in wishing to confront these tyrants, we imagined summoning a superhero's powers. Mo didn't have superpowers to confront the gang, he did so with his resolve. The gangstas rollin' on Mo that night had no idea of his resolve. When countless others gave up the goods, Mo said no.

What they did to Mo was the ultimate cowardice. They pulled the trigger because they couldn't conceive of a man standing on his own two telling them, "You cannot have what is mine." If you are not used to the light, when you see it you are blinded by it. This is why they used a gun. They were angry at Mo's light, his resolve. A man pure of heart is never intimidated. On the contrary, you are intimidated by him because you start to feel things lacking within yourself.

The point made at the end of the film, *Friday*, is also divine: Fight with your fists. You may win some and you may lose some, but you will continue to live your life. Unfortunately, the

"Summer of Violence" didn't have a Hollywood ending. Cube's "My Summer Vacation" was a more apt portrayal of Eastside Denver in 1993. That day long ago when Mo and his classmates received a lecture from DPD Officers in middle school instilled fear in many. The Colorado Rockies were in their inaugural season in '93 which meant everyone wanted to sport the gear however, when the officers were done with their spiel, one could think that anyone sporting a CR hat was an anarchist. The officers had nothing but good intentions and yet, a natural byproduct of their speech was indeed fear. Circumstances notwithstanding, Mo and his peers still had to live in the shit, and deal with these gangstas day in and day out. But living in fear is not living life as a celebration. For Mo, every basketball game was a sermon.

We say '93 until infinity, and so each generation must choose what to accept, what to deny, and what to pay forward. A cacophony of Baby Boomer voices still inundates us with virtues we may or may not agree with. The tragedy is we didn't get to see what Mo would become, for at a minimum, he was already on the path of serving his community and comfortable with being a role model. Basketball coach or Director of a Rec? There is no higher responsibility than letting the children play.

Tom Brokaw wrote extensively about the Greatest Generation. Saul Williams says the greatest Americans haven't been born yet. Two opposing opinions from two equally intriguing arguments. Mo never imagined millennials, for he would never see the millennium, nor Y2K, nor witness its subsequent absurdity. This is the conundrum, the realization that Mo is trapped in 1993 yet timeless in the same breath. '93 is just a marker, a blip on the radar signifying a change in consciousness for Mo. A millennial now shares his name, proving Geranimo Maestas was the penultimate, forever teaching generations both old and new about peace and resolve. We support the Movement, we support peace, but we forget about the resolve. Resolve is showing your true face when you don't have a father. Resolve is the realization that intimidation sprouts from insecurities. Mo's resolve was the same response our Indigenous ancestors had to the government trying to impose on and steal Native lands: they fought to the death. Belief is part of resolve too, for they believed horses were gifts from the Creator to help them in the battle of protecting their people, lands and sovereignty, just as belief made Mo stand up for his jacket, for this was his home too.

Indoctrination of colonialism, and even imperialism, are mentalities which become so deeply ingrained within us that we actively create gang territories. And these realities are so morose and conflated, they're similar to a kid on the playground drawing a line in the sand saying, "Don't cross this line." The line doesn't exist. All the lines and borders and names of countries on maps are from this single fallacy. Native Americans consider themselves inhabitants of the Earth. We essentially have no more of a right to claim the earth than an ant does. Now imagine the fallacy of paying rent to live on the earth. From birth we are indoctrinated in geography, and which countries we can play with and which ones we can't. Again, similar to kids in a sandbox with a parent telling them which kids they can play with and which ones they can't. The end game of imperialism is to draw more lines and claim more territories and wield a bigger influence than anybody else. Don't cross this line sounds like gangstas and gang territories. They don't own the land economically, but they own and regulate the presence of said land. They intimidate you until you acknowledge their occupation. They will take the goods they need whether or not they are yours. But imperialism is also semantics, so it is difficult to revolt against when cycles repeat because the terms may change, and the lines blur.

What does centuries-long indoctrination and fights for lines have to do with Mo's murder? Everything. Mo would want us to disarm the very psychology that keeps us killing each other.

Mexico once occupied from Texas to Canada to California

until it became the United States. And its people—and their subsequent generations thereafter—may feel a different sort of occupation. This is the reason Corky Gonzales taught the people about the Treaty of Guadalupe Hidalgo. It was the breaking of terms on behalf of the United States government. One of many broken terms to a people not to mention "The Trail of Broken Treaties" highlighted by activist Russell Means.

There were many protests opposing the Vietnam War. Artists, musicians, and athletes all opposed the reason we were at war. This recalls trumpeter Freddie Hubbard and avant-garde composer İlhan Kemaleddin Mimaroğlu's *Sing Me A Song of Songmy* album, released in 1971. The pair of musicians—and with the direction and insistence of Hubbard—planned to make a statement on the atrocities of war, specifically the Vietnam War, and did they ever. *Songmy* refers to the My Lai Massacre where US Troops executed over 400 unarmed Vietnamese people. America opposed communism, and so lines all the way across the world had to be reestablished. Songmy also touches on the Kent State victims, who were gunned down protesting the bombing of Cambodia, and the Tate and LaBianca killings. Peace was the end goal, while musically giving the pain and atrocity of war a sound, as if these horrific events had a soundtrack.

The original cover of *Sing Me A Song Of Songmy* is an interesting one, because it leaves its own trail of protesting nonstop imperialism through representations of art. Picasso's 1951 painting, *Massacre of Korea*, is on display underneath the album's header, further accentuating the protests of Hubbard and Mimaroglu against imperialism. This time the massacre is Sinchon, North Korea. The year, 1950.

Just because gangs created a culture of jacking teenagers for their goods, didn't mean that Mo had to succumb to their demands. Some might be of the opinion to give up the goods and to stay alive. This would have left Mo in a constant state of victimhood, instead Mo is eternal, both hero and sage. He never bowed down to a gang. He was never afraid of a gun or afraid of being outnumbered. What he did on that cold November night still baffles us. He was willing to stand up for us all because we were victimized, and they threatened our community. He lifts us when we're down and out, he lifts us eternally. This is the meaning of Movement. Mayans and Aztecs incorporated *Ollin*—Movement—into their culture and days. They saw it as a form of life, and it is. We are in concert with the wind, ebbing consistently, tree branches and its leaves dancing, flowing. Our immature minds and rudimentary understanding tell us that we are separate from both the trees and wind, when in actuality, we are touching all, so we move with the wind and dance with the trees. Life is movement and thus, Mo is constantly moving through us; we move his essence from our thoughts and prayers. The elders said, "Every happy thought is a prayer," so quantum entanglement anchors Mo's memory in our lives.

You don't have to be confident or congenial or competitive like Mo. Just remember that in a mere 16 years Mo remained confident and congenial and competitive despite the obstacles in his life. It's something to affirm on. *Ollin* has transformed to "all-in." The intent remains after hundreds of years. We are more powerful than we think. Mo is Generation X. X is infinity. Restin' on them 7's within infinite possibilities. His murder, this very story of Mo is also a possibility, a realm of understanding. His face a symbol of peace. His name a renaming of our future. His essence now beyond three dimensions.

The paradox is that no matter how much peace is in your heart, with constant pressure and altercation, militancy becomes you. To think this malapropos, you've probably never lived behind enemy lines, nor resided in any gang territory. Sooner or later, when you're pushed into a corner and you have nothing else but the pushback; death becomes you.

REGRETS

BEFORE I KNEW IT, MY FEET felt cemented to the ground and the vigils passed me like the Light Rail. "Next year," I would tell myself, but November rolled around again and I would always be busy. Maybe subconsciously I wanted myself to be busy. To avoid the hurt, to avoid the hole, to avoid seeing Mo's face again. Next year turned into 5 years, 10 years, 15, still, I always thought I had time. Twenty years came and passed and I kept running from that ambiguous feeling I had after my dad read me the *Rocky Mountain News* that morning. I would build myself up, and tell my wife that I was gonna go, that it was time I came out of the shadows, but I quickly turned against myself in my own head. Self-doubt is a killer. Questions would bury me alive in my own pity, questions like, "Where were you all this time?" "What happened to you?" "Why weren't you at the funeral?" I projected these questions from my own insecurities, imagining them flying out the mouths of those closest to Mo, and it led to nothing but lost time. Mo's family carried the biggest burden every day of their lives. How could I tell them it was too hard, that I never really dealt with it, that I withheld many great stories about Mo that they would have loved to hear. And this could be true, I believed they would accept me, but the truth was, that I didn't accept myself, that I was still jealous of Jay Medina and that I was still hung up on what people thought, as opposed to being present, being helpful, and most of all, paying tribute to my friend.

We moved back to Las Vegas in the summer of 2013 and I thought I would be free of this weight. I thought I could write one anecdote of me, Mo and Pablo having fun at the drive-in, send it to Cathy around the anniversary of his passing and that everything would be soirée. Instead, the opposite happened. The more physical space between me and Denver, the more I began to see Mo's face. I would see it at night before I went to bed. I would see it while driving to work on the 215. I saw it and knew I was still running and that I would run forever until I made an effort to reach out to Cathy. I also realized that Cathy couldn't save me. Even if she did forgive me for being absent for twenty-five years, I would have to forgive myself. That's when I started talking to my family and friends about Mo. They seemed happy, invigorated and interested in this man who had made such an impact on me and many other peoples' lives. I immediately started feeling better. No longer was I protecting this sacred wound deep inside of me. Now I was witnessing the power of paying it forward by honoring Geranimo with the power of the word.

Emiliano Zapata said, "the land belongs to those who work the land." And although Cathy was not a homeowner, she tilled the soil and tended to the souls of the Denver streets, the ancient apactl. She tilled them before Mo was born and she tills them today with a bigger purpose. As soon as I realized this reality regret melted away and I had an overwhelming urge to help Cathy in any way possible. Mo is Denver, Mo is Aztlan. Cathy is Denver, Cathy is Aztlan. We are Denver, we are Aztlan.

25 TO LIFE

Gregorian calendar. November 26, 2018, touching base with Cathy.

"Hi Cathy."

"How ya doin' mijo?"

"I'm good. We're gettin' ready to head down there in a bit but I still haven't heard back from Pablo."

"That's okay, mijo, this thing is a divine appointment. Whoever shows up tonight is meant to be there."

"You're absolutely right. I won't worry about it then. See ya soon."

* * *

TWENTY-FIVE YEARS to the day since my homie, Geranimo Maestas, was murdered for his Broncos jacket. The date was November 26, 1993. He was sixteen. Tonight, we gather at the spot he crossed over. East 33rd Avenue, between Williams and High Streets on the East Side of Denver. Steph and I arrive and see Cathy in a Denver Broncos Starter Jacket, an exact replica of the one Mo wore twenty-five years ago when he was fatally shot.

Introductions and reintroductions are made. I hope the physical distance from Vegas compensates for the distance in time I was gone from Mo's family and the *No 'Mo Violence Movement*. Mo's sister, La, says she doesn't remember me, but I can't blame her, twenty-five years is a lifetime. Before I get a second to dwell, Mo's brother, Ray, pops up with his vintage smile and gives everyone bear hugs.

A man with strong cheekbones and a beanie cap stands in the alley. Focusing on beams of light from an idling tow truck, he dons a pin on his collar, a school photograph of Mo from the 8th grade. A solitary man with solitary memories about the friend taken away in the night. We stand next to the man watching Ray corral his son, Marcus, then carry him away. I introduce us to the gent.

"Hello, I'm Gabe."

"Ambrose."

"This is my wife, Stephanie."

"Nice to meet you."

"Hey, you're Ambrose?"

"Gabe?"

"I remember you, man! I remember riding our bikes all the way to pick you up. Mo used to say 'We gotta go get Gabe from the North Side.'"

"I remember you too, brother. But I remember it was always 'Zeke and Ambrose.' Who is Zeke?"

"Zeke is my younger brother. You know Mo, it didn't matter your age or what not, he had us all kickin' it together."

"Yes indeed. See, that was the thing about Mo, it didn't matter where you were from, your race, nothin'. He merged people together from all sides of the city, this is livin' proof."

"True. It's been a long time, man, I've been out here every year since he passed."

"This is our first time, bro. We flew out from Vegas to be here. I've been gone for twenty-five but I'm here now."

"How'd you end up in Vegas?"

"Long story short, work. But a few years ago I started seeing Mo's face morning, noon and night. I would wake up in the morning feeling his energy, but also feeling empty, like I never really dealt with it, but through all that I finally realized my voice and how I can contribute to the Movement."

"That's tight, man. You know I went back, right?"

"What?"

"Remember Gilliam?"

"Oh shit! Hell yeah I do, I spent one night in that place and told myself I didn't belong there. Remember the terrace over-looking the city with the chain-link fence on all sides? We waited out in the cold while dudes went in the courtroom. Some came out with life."

"I went in on purpose."

"Nah . . . really?!"

"I heard he was there so I conjured a plan to get myself thrown in there. I ain't have no affiliation or nothin'. I went on a solo mission, fool."

"He was there?"

"Yeah, they had him separate from the rest of us but I didn't care. During our hour free time I went straight for his cell. I was bangin' on it and shit. Yellin' at him to come out. The guard was like 'You crazy?!! You know who that is?!!'"

I said, "Fuck yeah I know who that is! That muthafucker killed my homie!"

"What happened?"

"I couldn't reach him, and he didn't come out. After that, when I got out I turned my life around."

"Word up, mane . . ."

The people don't want to come out either. I can see their lights glowing from the freezing cold. They hear us but still won't come out. We're marching between their front yards and hybrid vehicles. A woman posts on Facebook: I didn't know there were gangs in Denver . . . Yes lady, and you moved right into the belly of the beast.

We're marchin'. Following the banner of Mo's likeness airbrushed onto white canvas. Ray doesn't remember who made it, but that they've had it for two decades now.

"WHAT DO WE WANT?"

"PEACE!"

"WHEN DO WE WANT IT?"

"NOW!"

"NO MO VIOLENCE,

NO MO VIOLENCE,

NO MO VIOLENCE!"

Three blocks later our tow-truck motorcade ends at a white building shrouded in nighttime. This is St. Charles Recreation Center, hallowed ground. "This is where Mo played Shawn 'Gee'," says Ambrose, eyes reddened from the memories. Aunts, uncles, cousins, nephews, nieces and friends take photos of the plaque hung on the wall in honor of Mo's dedication to his community. Marcus launches shots from his small frame like a catapult and the reverberation from multiple basketballs off the gym floor soothes the spirit. This is the center, the root.

Ray, Steph and I sit on a wooden bench while children continue to heave basketballs across the horizon. Ray's magnanimous character draws us in as our conversation cascades from dance discipline to Zen and the like. Cathy claims Jesus Christ as her Lord and Savior. Ray leaves no stone unturned. It gives me a deeper appreciation to the duality and uniqueness of Ray and Cathy's dynamic mother-son relationship. They know Mo's story includes both the wisdom of the esoteric and the tradition of Catholicism, and even more so our indigenous spirituality, yet they love each other just the same. Ray's words are sweet to my ears, I'm looking at him as if he were my younger brother, proud that he's on the path.

The heat from the center gets our blood pumping again but

then we scatter. It's a work night, a school night, and cold. Exiting the Center, we flurry back to life with heavy hearts. Across the cul-de-sac, Mo's cousin, Marcelo, is standing as a silhouette in front of a monster tow truck. The director of this motorcade, doing his part in this ambiance of dedication. His arms are crossed, and he looks at the gleam of the Center behind me, and with it the hopes of the fallen soul that once graced its doors.

We pile into Cathy's van as she gives us a ride back to our rental. Steph rides shotgun while Ray and Marcus sit on the floor in the back of the van. I'm in the middle seat looking out the sliding door's window, thinking about how after Mo moved out of the neighborhood, he consistently came back to pluck me out of that world and show me something different. I think about how we met, and those two glorious years we spent together on the other side of downtown, off the parallel of Pecos Street, over on the North Side of things.

OFRENDA

THEY LOVE POKING FUN AT our sixth sun prophecy while simultaneously preparing for catastrophe. Whether you believe there's an underground bunker under DIA or not, or whether you believe its haunting murals are foretelling us something or not, the foray still depicts a brown child being greeted by the razor's edge of a machete, wielded by a gas-masked, police-stated guard. Coming or going, this image has greeted us for years at the baggage claim. You can look it up on YouTube or find the mural when you arrive. It's ever present, modernized colonialism in plain sight.

They moved Servicios de la Raza out the North Side. Shuttered Escuela Tlatelolco and Rishel. Bounced my family off that Denver pavement. Entrenched dispensaries where parks once stood. Replaced empanadas with palm pies. (Ask Bobby) Exchanged brown babies for dogs. Painted over murals of Aztlan. Voted down an initiative to rename Columbus Park, Columbus/La Raza Park.

Yes, we owned North Denver and thrived, never imagining a non-brown North Side. Gentrification is real, but some of the onus must be on our own misguided youth. When we weren't

185

there for them, they turned to gangs. We gunned down each other in the same streets named after ancestral tribes that were massacred. Zuni, Pecos, Tejon, Shoshone. But Mo never apologized for being himself. He never apologized for his indigeneity. Sixteen years of brilliance was ended by envy, greed, deceit, hate. Caught in the crossfire of our bright future and tumultuous past.

We coveted material things. Then killed for them.

Even from the grave Mo will have his say, immortal in the spirit of a Brown Beret. Though they try to paint over us again. Erasure again in effect, we have reinforcements on the streets. The *No 'Mo Violence Cultural Dance Group* on those Denver streets. It doesn't matter how many doors are shuttered in the troops' faces. We're resourceful. "Hell, I gotta kitchen with some nice tile, mijo, we can practice right here, right now," Cathy tells me.

I don't care how it happened. I want to fight and mourn and cry. I want to skydive at 30,000 feet and grab a patch of cumulous cause my friend will be there. Or maybe he's in the ground. "Ashes to ashes and dust to dust." Or maybe he's in the Denver streets. Maybe he's present in the plaque overlooking St. Charles Recreation Center. Or maybe Mo's in all of us, you and me.

For 1993, and especially today, we keep on with the spirit of a Brown Beret. Why are we so quick to deny the genocide of the indigenous peoples of this continent? Why were they so quick to paint Mo's murder as territorial gang violence? But we are his memory. And to the next generation: Ready yourselves for the fight. You will face unprecedented evil. Or maybe, this fight is all there is and all there ever will be. Clear yourself of debt but remember our ancestors didn't believe in land ownership. We live on the Earth; we are her children. Question everything they tell you. Question your indoctrination.

* * *

Officer McCurley pulls up to the corner of 37th & Lafayette and looks to his right. Mo's mural is one of the last images he sees before his impending retirement. The piece is only weeks old and lines the back wall of St. Charles Recreation Center. Over the years Cathy won over the officers of the DPD. Her intent was pure. "We couldn't save them both," McCurley blurted that fateful night. Yet Cathy was focused, focused on doing whatever it took to save the next youth.

"I guess the motherfucker wasn't affiliated after all."

"What the hell are you talking about, McCurley?"

"That spic kid in '93, you know, the no more violence kid."

Who really won that night? But you need to be wise to see it. Is it the earthly bound forces of desire and possessions? Or is it the love that is out of time? A love that is past, present and future, a timeless love. Mo is an ageless body and a timeless mind. Mo is the spark that ignites us. A love that was there before and a love that will be here after. Unbound by earth, it's God at work.

The foundation of motherhood La La displays, symbolizing power like a Brown Beret. They scrutinize the number 13 and simultaneously study Chaco Canyon and Palenque for clues to the stars. When you know your ancestors travelled from Pleiades, mapped visible and invisible stars, predicted the elliptical galaxy, and harnessed nuclear fission energy from Mercury under Mexica pyramids they can't call you undocumented anymore. They're skilled—overqualified—in the practice of doublespeak, because they'll call you an alien to your face when all the while they study your ancestors behind your back for keys to the universe. Ancient knowledge has been suppressed. When archeologists discover an elongated skull from Mexico the Smithsonian rears its grubby little hands and snatches it. Poof! It's gone. But the Maya knew—rightly—that there were five civilizations before us.

Unless you know Native American history, you don't know

America. Period. I don't care how patriotic you are or claim to be. The Navajo code talkers saved us all.

The divinity of dancing we witness from Ray, with the tact and precision of a Brown Beret. Aztlan is relative, and deep as you want to go. It's everything and everybody. It has layers. Cahokia, Woodhenge, Chaco Canyon. People all concur that heaven is a place, that hell is a place. When we say "go to hell" we imagine the worst conditions. But if you invoke Aztlan they say it is fantasy. But kneeling to the Lord, Cathy will pray, with the devoutness and devotion of a Brown Beret.

IN A TALK I HAD WITH CATHY she didn't dominate the conversation but took charge of it profoundly and wisely, saying it made sense that Mo was weighing heavy on my mind all these years later, reiterating the fact that after Mo's murder, most of us teenagers desperately needed counseling which we never received. This shook me. Here I was talking to the mother of my deceased friend, and she's worried about *me*? I was floored. Then I told her my idea for the book, and if I can have her permission to write it. Stepping out on faith, she said yes without a hesitation or pause. Unequivocally, yes! She didn't ask me how many books I have written. Although she didn't remember me, she didn't worry about my validity. She didn't make me jump through hoops, and she didn't ask to see my credit score. She jumped out on faith: just like that! I hope to live my life as fully as Cathy does, trusting that God will right all, that He has the plan although we may not be privy to view it. My friend Roger says I tend to "oversell." Cathy had already given me her blessing, but I still pushed, offering to send her two chapters I wrote and she quickly declined, saying, "No mijo, I wanna read it when it's done."

And with that single statement, she instilled in me a trust that was liberating. I could now craft the book—Mo's eulogy—with no provisions, accentuating the highest of highs and the lowest of lows. The pure, unadulterated truth, no matter how deep or hurtful or tragic the content.

I asked her about the long-awaited plaque.

"The Denver Parks and Recreation ain't trying to spend no money on Mo's plaque. They ain't gonna spend the money to mount it properly. But the workers went ahead and tacked it up anyway with a long nail," Cathy admits. During our stay on Mo's 25th vigil, I took a photo of the plaque. Mo's eyes as vibrant now as they were back then. Much props to those that made it happen. Much props to St. Charles for having it hung. Much props to the Parks & Recreation for having the wherewithal to recognize greatness in the community; but when I pulled up the photo of the plaque a month later, I realized it was misspelled. Community is misspelled. It reads "commuity." We're gonna hold onto it though. We have to. Cathy fought long and hard to get it up, and Mo's face dons 3777 N. Lafayette Street. Forever restin' on them 7's.

Cathy and I joke about how we reunited, that morning when I called out of the blue. I dialed the number I got off Facebook and didn't have a clue of how I would be greeted. But it happened the way it was supposed to, true to who Mo was, and his everlasting story.

"Hello, I'm tryin' to reach Cathy."

"Yes, this is Cathy, who's this?"

"It's Gabe Patterson."

"Who?"

"Gabe Patterson, Mo's friend."

"You need to be more specific, baby, my son had hundreds of friends . . ."

ACKNOWLEDGMENTS

All praise due to the Most High God. To My Love, Steph, thank you for always believing in me. When I told you about my idea for the book you were all-in from the jump. Thank you for your love, guidance, and resourcefulness. I couldn't have done it without you. To Cathy, you blessed this project from beginning to end, thank you for allowing me to tell Mo's story. Not only did our conversations result in major plots of the book, but you continue to teach me how to walk in faith, thank you, friend. To Ricky N Lala, thank you guys for your enthusiasm and dedication to this book, it means so much to me. To Ray Ray, thank you for vouching for me and allowing me part of your amazing journey. You reminded me of things I forgot about long ago, thank you for your help. To Ambrose Moreno, our conversation was the foundation for key points of the book. Thank you for sharing your insight and passion. To Pries, you again stole the show with your beautiful artwork. Thank you for blessing this book with your talent. To Valerie, thank you for all you do, I am eternally grateful. To my Mom, Eleanor Patterson, the original Shazam, (breakin' down samples since '91) thank you for allowing me to explore the world on my own at an early age. To my Dad, Randy Patterson, thank you for encouraging me to "push the pen, not the shovel." Thank you to the Wells family, the Zamora family, the Tate family, the Jacobs family, the Walters family, the Hedrich family, and the Varela family. Thank you to Eric, Eddie, and Ang. To Sharon, thanks for the Fiverr plug! Thank you to Noel, Flip, John, Spoke, Cisco M., Cisco R., Steve, and Chonz. Thank you to the entire Colorado Hip Hop family. To Syntax Vernac, thank you for staying ghetto gold. To Valdo, you inspire me to be better. To The Temple of Hip Hop, thank you for overstanding this existence. To Shep, thank you for explaining why this needed to be a memoir. To Rob Avila, thank you for being willing to jump right in and help. To Rubén Degollado, thanks for being willing to hop on a call and help a brother out, you also affirmed on the memoir point of view. To Brady, thank you for your attention to detail. Rest in Peace to Keith Patterson. To my Grandparents, who remain in my consciousness and heart, Gloria Patterson, Simon Orlando Varela, and Ricarda Varela, I acknowledge that your sacrifices ultimately allowed me to act on my dreams, and I thank you. To my kids, Maya, Isaiah, and Ash, always remember that you can do anything you put your mind to, you just have to believe in yourself.

Connect with me:
gabepatterson77.com

facebook.com/gabriel.patterson.5
twitter.com/GabePatterson77

Gabriel Patterson was born and raised in Denver, Colorado. He now lives in Las Vegas, Nevada, and is next up in the emcee to author pipeline. This is his first book.

Geranimo "Mo" Maestas

Role Model in the Commuity
Killed by Gang Violence in 1993

10/30/77 - 11/26/93

9 781736 607206